THE BIOLOGY OF THE SPIRIT

Also by Edmund W. Sinnott

TWO ROADS TO TRUTH

CELL AND PSYCHE

The Biology
of the Spirit

by Edmund W. Sinnott

NEW YORK · 1955

The Viking Press

514.01
Si 6 l

33, 301
February, 1956

Contents

Contents

Foreword

This is an unorthodox book—unorthodox in its main thesis, and especially in the implications that it draws from this thesis. Many biologists will be offended by its support of the reality of purpose in living things, and thus of teleology. Psychologists will be displeased by its insistence that motives come from biological goal-seeking rather than from "drives." It will irritate many philosophers by the simple way in which it disposes of the mind-body relationship through deriving both of these parts of man from the same organic process. The biological basis it proposes for the soul and for the human spirit will not satisfy most theologians. Students of aesthetics and of ethics may regard as too naïve the argument that both the beautiful and the right have their roots in protoplasm. Some men of faith will be disappointed with the foundation for a satisfying religious philosophy the book attempts to lay in the facts of the life sciences. That a student of biology should try to find within his own field the answers to such deep questions will seem to many a hopeless undertaking, the attempt of an over-confident enthusiast to discuss philosophical ideas beyond his competence.

In the solution of man's major problems, however, biology is bound to be increasingly involved, for man is an organism and everything about him has its physical basis in the living stuff of which he is composed. Biology should not be bounded by observations and experiments on the structure, activities, and evolutionary history of animals and plants. It ought to pursue bigger game than this. *All* problems of life ultimately are biological ones, and the facts with which the student of organisms deals should be explored not for themselves alone but for the suggestions they may offer for the more complex phenomena of life.

Although its conclusions are opposed to various orthodoxies, the present volume does have a consistent basic idea. It attempts to relate all aspects of the psychical life of man to the biological fact of self-regulation. This regulatory character of living things, evident in the way in which the organism in development moves so inexorably to its consummation and coordinates its activities so precisely to a norm, may be regarded as a primitive sort of goal-seeking and thus a manifestation of mind. A number of distinguished biologists have called attention to this similarity between the mental and the developmental in living things, and a good case can be made out for the origin of both in biological purposiveness. Some of the evidence in support of this idea has been marshaled here.

There are several implications of this concept that seem to the author to be especially significant. That development and behavior—leading to body and mind—are two aspects of the same basic process, one as real as the other, like the two sides of a coin, is clearly opposed to the philosophy of dualism. If goal-seeking is fundamental in biology, the importance of *intention* in determining behavior should also be emphasized more than psychologists commonly do. The present discussion, however, carries the argument for the biological origin of psychical activities still further and seeks to derive that nebulous aspect of man, his spirit, from these same regulatory processes. It regards spirit as the mass of natural impulses, desires, and emotions that well up out of protoplasmic purposiveness, setting up in us goals and longings of all sorts, conscious or unconscious. These are native to our living stuff, though subject to elevation or debasement. Such a concept provides a foundation for a philosophical system that puts goal-seeking in a central position and finds a place there for spiritual values, for the soul, and for God.

Here evidently the author is launching out into water that is very deep. He has laid himself open to attack both by those who regard such a philosophy as far too tenuous for a robust religion, and by those who see the whole idea as hopelessly mystical, an abandonment of the ancient and time-tested concepts of the sciences by one whose training should have taught him better. Whether these criticisms are justified or whether the suggestions offered here will be of any value in unifying our ideas about man and in reconciling the opposing ways in which science and religion often look at life must remain for the reader to determine. We can all agree that in these profound problems every sincere attempt at a solution should be welcomed.

The basic idea of this book is the one presented in the author's earlier *Cell and Psyche,* although its implications for philosophy and religion are here developed much more fully.

Quotations from various writers made in these pages have been duly acknowledged, and for the use of them the author wishes to offer his most sincere thanks.

THE BIOLOGY OF THE SPIRIT

CHAPTER I

Man's Double Nature

Abstract

The ancient question as to what the relation is between the material part of man—his body—and the immaterial portion that inhabits it—his mind or his soul—has long perplexed philosophers. The traditional belief that these are separate things and that man's immaterial part is real and is independent of his body was shaken by the theory of evolution. It has been even more gravely challenged by the conclusions of modern biology, which regards the body as a material mechanism obeying the laws of chemistry and physics and requiring no psychical element to direct it. These changed conceptions of man's nature have seriously disturbed his ideas about himself and his relation to the universe, and underlie much of the confusion and pessimism in the world today. An attempt will here be made to find in the basic facts of biology itself a common foundation for both mind and body. This will make it possible to interpret them as parts of the underlying unity of life.

On a far distant evening lost in the mists of time a hairy ape-man, crouched in the smoky firelight of his family cave, began to wonder dimly about something beyond the urgent necessities of food and safety. Perhaps his chattering mate that day had added one more member to the circle squatting around the fire. Perhaps not long ago his comrade had been seized and dragged away to be devoured by a cave bear or a sabertooth. Perhaps last night he had dreamed of someone long since dead. Vague questions about these happenings began to trouble him, and gropingly he turned them over in his mind. This was a new experience, for matters of this sort are never of concern to any brute. In pondering them, the apelike creature was becoming man.

Doubtless among the earliest questions rising in his foggy brain were ones about himself. How did he differ from the aurochs and the mastodon? Where did he fit into the great world of trees and beasts and stars, of fire and food, of light and darkness, pain and birth and death? Whence came his children, and what fate was there in store for them and him? Where were his old comrades, whom he saw no more? What meant the strange and often terrifying fantasies that came to him in sleep? Such questions more and more assailed him now.

In the long ages since that day we have continued the search for answers to them, framing them more clearly and reasoning about them more intelligently than our progenitors could ever do, but still without reaching any sure conclusions. Today we ask them even more insistently. Pope's admonition that "the proper study of mankind is man" is now more strictly heeded than it ever was before. At every level man is subject to our active scrutiny. The bones of his ancestors have been dug up to reconstruct the evolutionary path by which he reached his present high estate. The multitude of processes in his material self have been examined with the sharp new tools of physiology. Psychology is uncovering the secrets of his mind. Anthropologists subject

the varied patterns of his social life to the same precise
examination that biologists give to colonies of ants or bees.
What his true nature is, the poet and philosopher and theologian have argued long and earnestly. Much has been
learned about him, but much more remains unknown. Man
still slips through the nets in which we hopefully attempt
to capture him. He is too complex to bind in any single
mold, too various for simple definition. A mixture of perplexing contradictions, he remains indeed "the glory, jest,
and riddle of the world."

Through all the centuries, however, one question more
than any other has perplexed explorers of the realm of
man—his strange double nature. The physical part of him,
his body, is born, lives, grows and dies, and finally is buried
in the dust. But governing that body there seems to be an
intangible something that can feel and think, a subtler
part of him which is the essence of his being, and which
some believe still lives on when the body is no more. Different aspects of it have been given different names—
"mind," "will," "soul," "spirit." Man seems to be two beings—a material one, and its immaterial counterpart. From
Plato's time to ours wise men have argued about the relation between the body and this mysterious tenant that inhabits it. Are they both "real," or is one of them no more
than an illusion? This strange dualism of body and mind,
matter and spirit, the tangible and the intangible within
us, is as great an enigma still as it was in the days of
ancient Egypt and the Greek philosophers. The different
answers that have been given to it lie at the heart of the
other differences that so divide the world today.

For ages man believed in this dualism of body and soul.
With an egotism almost sublime he thought of himself as
a special sort of being, the center and climax of the uni-

verse, after whose creation God had rested and brought the cosmic process to a close; he thought of himself not as a body only but as an immortal soul, the saving or perdition of which was his chief concern and a matter of moment even to God himself. Such a concept was long taken for granted in our Western world. There was much discussion, to be sure, as to the details of man's nature and his destiny, but these deep problems were generally left to the philosophers and theologians. About them science had little then to say.

In the past hundred years, however, traditional beliefs have been profoundly shaken by the new concepts about man and nature that have come from the development of biology and the other sciences. First was the challenge of the theory of evolution. Man had not been specially created, said this new doctrine, nor was he the result of any recognizable prevision. Indeed, his origin and that of all other living things seemed to have come about as the result of natural, not supernatural, processes, by chance and not by design. He was nothing but an animal, after all, and entitled to no more consideration than any beast of the field might fairly claim.

Evidence to support man's animal origin is overwhelming. Anatomically he is obviously a primate and not radically different from the higher apes. His brain has no distinctively human features. Fossil remains of many sorts have now been found that are clearly more primitive than modern man and closer to the apes. Darwin's theory of natural selection made clear for the first time how all evolutionary changes could have been brought about, and thus made plausible the concept that the origin of man himself is due to the same processes that gave rise to other species. The impact of this idea on all our thinking was tremendous. If one looks for the greatest drama of the nineteenth century he will not find it in the rise of popular government around the world or in the spread of the industrial revolution, important as these were, but in something more profound—the challenge that science then threw down to old ideas about the origin, nature, and destiny of man. The world still staggers from the shock of it, and no small part of today's confusion and of the doubts that many have about man's dignity and worth has come from the crumbling of old beliefs as to what he really is.

All this was disquieting enough, but the development of modern biology, especially genetics, biochemistry, and physiology, raised even graver doubts. These sciences owe their spectacular progress to the assumption that all the processes of life can be interpreted finally as simply physical and chemical ones. Many of them have been imitated in the laboratory test-tube. The actions of enzymes, hormones, nucleic acids, complex proteins, and other substances concerned with the processes of life in general, so far as science can analyze them, follow the same laws that govern all the lifeless universe. To many the conclusion is now obvious that man, like every other living thing, is only a material mechanism, extraordinarily complex but no different in his basic nature from any other piece of machinery. This conception readily solves the dilemma of man's dual nature by denying that the intangible mental and spiritual side of him really exists at all.

In this confusion some of the questions that so concerned our grandfathers and were for them the center of interrogation and debate have lost their former urgency. Many of the attributes that man once seemed to have appear in modern eyes to be mere fictions, unreal and worthy of no serious attention. The Mind, for example, used to be thought of as a distinct thing with a nature and laws of its own. Psychologists do speak of the mind still, but in a rather figurative way. Sensations and reactions are the matters that concern them now; memory, conditioning, ,thought, and learning are the basis of much earnest study; but Mind, the word with a capital letter, has been demoted from the high place it once held. Indeed, radical psychologists deny the existence of anything that needs to be described by such a name at all. The sum of a person's activities, of his behavior, is all there is, they say. These, like any natural phenomena, can best be studied from the outside by strictly objective methods and are to be described in purely physical terms. The strange ideas about "mind" that men have gained by the outmoded use of introspection, of looking within at their own fallible sensations and experiences, such authorities regard as illusions that have come down from prescientific days.

So is it too with the Will. Men used to train their wills and were proud of them. The dominant and successful owed their eminence in large measure, as they thought, to the force of strong wills. But today you may look in vain through most textbooks of psychology for even a mention of the will. The very word has almost vanished from technical vocabularies. It is obviously meaningless for a scientific orthodoxy that regards man's actions not as rising from his own determination but as the result of inborn or environmental forces which push this way and that a being who no longer can be thought of as his own master. The freedom of the will, a major problem in an earlier day, has thus for many lost its meaning.

But the part of man that most concerned the earlier students of his nature and destiny was something far more vital, his Soul. This was his particular treasure, the real essence of his being. The danger of its "loss" was harrowing to think of, and "saving" it became his life's chief task. For the psychology of today, however, the soul has gone the way of those other intangible attributes of man upon which modern conceptions of his nature cast such doubt. What is there, we may ask, that distinguishes the soul of man from the breath of life common to every creature? Where in his long evolutionary history did he cease to be a beast without a soul and become a human being that possessed one? An ovum certainly lacks a soul, but when in the development of an embryo does the soul appear? Such questions seem irrelevant to many, since they are concerned with something that appears to have no basis in reality. Religious orthodoxy still maintains the existence and significance of the human soul, as do many thoughtful men outside the fold of faith, but in discussions of man's nature it no longer occupies the center of the stage as once it did.

And yet it is on these immaterial aspects of man that the deepest of his problems are centered. The body, tough and tangible but also temporal, he can readily accept as real, but he has always been inclined to think of the more nebulous spiritual part of him in terms of timeless and transcendent values, as something through which he held communion with the universe. Repercussions from the new ideas about himself, which cast grave doubt on the existence of such qualities, have wrought confusion in his thinking. The concept of a spirit in man has been so closely tied to that of a greater Universal Spirit that loss of belief in one has often meant a loss of faith in the other also. The convinced evolutionist who has felt obliged to abandon his belief in man's divinity has generally abandoned his belief in all divinity as well. A mechanistic interpretation of man's life, expressed though it may be in terms of high idealism, is bound to rob man of much of his former dignity, worth, and freedom, and the universe becomes thereby a bleaker and more inhospitable place. Men are divided selves and often know not whether to pay homage to the body and its delights or to the spirit and its very different set of values. In such confusion it is no wonder that neuroses and other maladies of the mind are steadily increasing and that the couch of the psychiatrist is rarely empty. Science has made many contributions to man's life and happiness and has given him a clearer picture of reality than he ever had before, but the disruption of his ancient faiths for which it is often held responsible has profoundly disturbed his attitude toward life.

Despite the difficulty of harmonizing the modern concept with the ancient views of man, a person who is blessed with healthy common sense, though necessarily accepting the obvious findings of the sciences, cannot help feeling that the philosophical conclusions so often drawn from them are too extreme. Just as the direct creation of Adam from the dust seems to him incredible, so does the idea that he himself is a machine, an automaton, without freedom, responsibility, or worth. If this is the inevitable conclusion to be drawn from modern science, he is likely to say, then science has not gone far enough along the road to a final understanding of what man really is.

The thoughtful scientist is troubled too. He is less likely now than he was a few decades ago to be dogmatic in his philosophy. The physicist and the astronomer have found that matter and energy and the universe are far more complex things than their Victorian forebears believed was possible. The proofs that matter is at last no more than energy, that the atom's once reassuring solidity is an illusion, that space is curved, and that the universe is expanding, are sobering. Even the biologist, who has but recently learned to use the physical sciences for the interpretation of his own field and has found them of enormous value there, is beginning to suspect that life may be more than the simple series of metabolic processes that some enthusiastic physiologists of fifty years ago believed it was. He still assumes that a living being is a system that follows the laws of physics and chemistry evident in a lifeless mechanism, but he rarely makes the prediction any more that a living cell will soon be synthesized.

We are standing at an impasse in our basic philosophy and seem to be faced with the necessity of a choice between the physical and the spiritual side of man as the final reality. Age-long efforts to find a reconciliation that will be scientifically acceptable and still preserve the essence of the older concepts have been unsuccessful, and in their personal philosophies many thoughtful people have thus been forced to lead double lives—one adapted to the practical affairs of a mechanistic world, and the other to those deeper intuitive and emotional feelings that speak with such commanding inner authority. Must this rift within us still continue, or can some way at last be found to heal it? I am persuaded that a satisfying harmony between these two attitudes, seemingly so diverse, is *not* impossible, and that it will be derived from illuminating insights into the nature. of life that have not yet been sufficiently explored. From that very science that was responsible for the disruption of the old conceptions of man's nature will come, I am bold enough to suggest, a means of restoring many of them within the framework of an orderly intellectual system. To accomplish this may seem an impossible task, but man's unhappy dualism is proving so disastrous, both for individuals and in its impact on society, that a study of every possible means of bringing together the two sides of him is worth investigating. It is to such an exploration that the following pages are directed.

That a biologist can contribute helpfully toward the solution of a problem that so long has baffled the thinkers of our race will seem to many quite improbable, and the attempt itself may appear to be an almost preposterous undertaking, one more example of a layman in philosophy who blunders into a problem far beyond his competence. The science of life, however, has not yet been examined deeply enough for the constructive ideas that can be gathered from it, and a biologist may be in a position to make suggestions that a philosopher might overlook. The area to be explored is a domain into which many have been tempted to rush without due preparation—and thus have met disaster—and which others find so full of snares and pitfalls that it is impossible to penetrate. He who enters it will always be in danger of violating one or another vested interest in science, philosophy, or religion, and must therefore be either a bold man or one no longer vulnerable to the perils that lurk in being heterodox. I am not unmindful of these dangers and can only quote what Sir Arthur Eddington once said in such a case: "The recent tendencies of science do, I believe, take us to an eminence from which we can look down into the deep waters of philosophy; and if I rashly plunge into them, it is not because I have confidence in my powers of swimming, but to try to show that the water is really deep." [1]

---

[1] *The Nature of the Physical World* (Cambridge: Cambridge University Press, 1929), p. 276.

CHAPTER II

Biological Goals

Abstract

The most difficult problem in biology is to discover how, in the development of an animal or plant, a precisely formed body and not a formless mass is produced.

Every living thing is an organized system, well named an "organism." Each part and function is so closely correlated with the rest that the whole develops in an orderly fashion toward the growth of the mature individual, as if to a "goal." If normal development is blocked or interrupted, the organism, particularly in its early stages and in lower types, shows a strong tendency to restore lost parts and regulate its growth processes so that it still can reach its goal. Each part, at least potentially, is able to restore the whole, so that the whole seems to be immanent in all its parts.

A series of examples of normal and of experimentally modified development in animals and plants are described to make these facts clear.

Although the problem of how man's mind can be related to his body soon ascends into the levels of psychology and philosophy, its roots must be anchored in biology. To try to solve it without taking account of the fundamental facts and concepts of the life sciences will prove a fruitless undertaking, for a human being, first of all, is a living organism. Biology in the broad sense cannot limit itself to a consideration of only the structures and activities of living things but must finally include *all* phenomena of life. It will need to deal with many things that cannot be analyzed in quantitative terms. As Agar has pointed out, "It is not only legitimate but necessary for [the biologist] to include in his explanatory schemes factors which are unnecessary for the explanatory schemes of the physicist—namely, such concepts as memory, anticipation, purpose, final causation —in a word, perception." [1] Philosopher and biologist both should learn to widen their horizons.

The basis of the attempt that is here made to find a unity beneath man's double nature is laid chiefly in a study of that portion of biology concerned with the facts of growth and development in living things. Here are the greatest unsolved problems in this science, and here are destined to be waged its most decisive battles in the future. Questions concerned with the familiar processes by which life is maintained—digestion, nutrition, respiration, and other activities in what is called metabolism—are difficult enough, but a direct attack on them through the techniques of chemistry and physics is making most encouraging progress. What guides the development of an animal or plant, however, so that a body is produced and not a formless mass, a body with a characteristic pattern and an organized structure, is far more difficult to understand. The same difficulty is present in such remarkable physiological regulations as those by which constant body temperature, blood sugar, and oxygen levels are maintained.

[1] W. E. Agar, *A Contribution to the Theory of the Living Organism* (Melbourne, Australia: Melbourne University Press, 1951), p. 235.

These problems have been actively considered by many, both biologists and philosophers. At the turn of the century a distinguished German embryologist, Hans Driesch, through the results of his experiments became so impressed with the difficulty of a purely mechanical explanation of developmental processes that he saw no alternative but to support the idea that there is a sort of non-material agent, or entelechy, in the organism, which directs its growth. Such a vitalistic philosophy is now held by few biologists and is quite unorthodox in a day when the whole tendency of the science of life is to explain its facts in terms of the known laws of chemistry and physics. Nevertheless, the serious difficulties in accounting for the phenomena of development and embryology, first emphasized by the experiments and discussions of Driesch, have never been satisfactorily met. Along most other lines of attack on the problems of life, biologists have made notable advances, but this particular bastion has stubbornly resisted their assaults.

In simple terms, the problem is this: Every living thing is an organized system, each part and function closely correlated with all the others. This is evident in many ways, but most conspicuously in the processes of growth and development. A plant or animal grows in an orderly fashion to a precise bodily form characteristic of the particular species to which it belongs, as toward a precise "goal." Growth is so nicely coordinated—faster in some directions, slower in others—that in all parts it keeps step until the final end is reached. Differences within the organism arise in orderly progression. Development is determined, we know, by thousands of inherited genetic units in each cell, but their actions are so nicely coordinated in timing and degree that only rarely do the normal processes become confused. All this is hard enough to understand, but the difficulty is greatly increased by the results of experiments in blocking or interrupting the usual course of development. Under these conditions the organism and its parts show a surprising ability to restore what has been lost, rearrange its normal processes of growth, and produce at last, often by circuitous courses, a whole and typical individual. The whole seems somehow immanent in all its parts. This regulatory capacity is present to a greater degree in some forms than in others, and varies with conditions. It is more evident in early stages of development than in later ones, but it vividly demonstrates the action of a co-ordinating control of some sort, which guides development to a definite culmination. A living thing is an organized and self-regulating system, well named an "organism." This is a fundamental fact in biology and the basis for regarding the life sciences as distinct from the physical ones.

To explain all this in terms of the sort of mechanism with which physics and chemistry have made us familiar is exceedingly difficult. The biologist refuses to invoke a mystical agent like a psyche or entelechy to account for these puzzling facts, but he has little to offer in its place save a firm faith that something will ultimately be discovered that can give the answer. Sir Charles Sherrington has well expressed this attitude. "Chemistry and physics," says he, "account for so much which the cell does, and for so much to which years ago physical science could at that time offer no clue, that it is justifiable to suppose that the still unexplained residue of the cell's behavior will prove resoluble by chemistry and physics." [2] Despite our substantial knowl-

[2] *Man on His Nature* (Cambridge: Cambridge University Press, 1941), p. 135.

edge of the activities that go on in the body, however, it must be admitted that as yet we have not even a plausible working hypothesis that can explain these regulated processes of development. This failure is embarrassing to biologists and is rarely discussed with the frankness it deserves. Nevertheless, at the very center of their science still sits this unsolved problem, a bolus of undigested, unexplained phenomena.

This integrating and directive control that guides bodily growth and development resembles in so many ways the equally unexplained directiveness of man's behavior which we call mental or psychic activity as to suggest the exciting possibility that these two may be expressions of the same underlying biological process. To understand one may help us understand the other. An exploration of this possibility perhaps can assist the philosopher to resolve the perplexing dualism of man's nature by interpreting its basis in biological terms and thus bringing into harmony the two aspects of him that now appear to be so very different.

The general facts of organization and self-regulation in the growth and development of plants and animals underlie the hypothesis to be presented here and must be understood if one is to follow the argument. Some of them are necessarily technical and involve ideas often unfamiliar to one not trained in the disciplines of biology. To present them as simply as possible, I shall therefore describe a series of examples of self-regulation, letting the facts speak for themselves. On the basis of the evidence thus offered, an attempt will then be made to extend this conception from the phenomena of the body to those of the mind.

The examples are taken both from normal developmental

histories and from those where there has been experimental interference with the normal course.

The Pattern in the Pine

A pine tree is as simple an organism as one can find, save among the lowliest of living things. It has few of the complexities of an animal—no stomach, no heart, no muscles, no nerves, no sense organs, and certainly no brain. Despite this, it possesses a bodily pattern to which it stubbornly adheres, maltreat it as you will. There is something within it that makes it a pine tree, and not only a pine tree but a white pine or a pitch pine or a red pine. This is evident, among many other ways, in the general bodily form by which you can recognize it when it is seen against the sky. Other trees have different patterns, and a skillful naturalist can identify them as far off as he can see them, by this trait alone.

How stoutly a pine tree resists attempts to modify its form, and how persistently it restores its normal pattern when this has been altered, may easily be shown by some simple experiments that anyone can make. There is a great advantage in working with a tree in problems of this sort, for you can get inside your specimen, so to speak, and manipulate it in various ways, without having to cut or injure it all. The only requirements are a piece of twine and the patience to wait a few months for results.

Before you begin to study a pine tree, observe how it grows. Pick out a young sapling—the white pine is a good species to work with—that is low enough so that you can keep watch on the buds at the tip. Early in May you will see these growing out into young shoots—one in the middle, and four or five others around it—all bunched in a

tight cluster and pointed straight up, "negatively geo-
tropic," as the botanist would say—growing directly away
from the center of the earth. Before long, however, this
cluster becomes looser. The central "leader" stays erect, but
the laterals begin to spread apart like the ribs of an umbrella that is being opened upside down. In June, when
these reach maturity, they have come to lie at an angle of
about seventy degrees to the main axis or trunk. This angle,
not a horizontal position, is their characteristic one for the
first few years.

If you truss these branches up in various ways to prevent
them from reaching this normal position you will see how
persistently the tree acts—I almost said "tries"!—to restore
its characteristic pattern.

First bind a cluster of growing terminal branches together with a loop around the whole about halfway down,
so that the umbrella cannot fully open. Though the lower
halves of each branch are thus held vertical, the free upper
portions act like typical branches and spread out until they
reach the normal angle with the leader. They have come as
close as they can to restoring the typical growth pattern of
the tree.

On another tree, pull down the growing leader from its
vertical position so that it lies at a right angle with the
trunk below, and tie it there. It will behave very differently from the side branches, and its growing tip will swing
back up again until it is pointed straight to the sky.

Now carry the experiment a step further. A lateral
branch at the beginning of its second year will continue
outward growth by its own leader, at the angle established
the first year. Before growth starts, pull one of these lateral
branches downward thirty or forty degrees by tying a
cord part way along it and fastening the other end to the

trunk below. Tie another lateral branch upward about the same amount. As the new shoots grow out from the ends of these laterals, you will find that they do not continue in the enforced directions of the branches from which they come, but that the new growth takes up an angle to the trunk that is characteristic for freely growing branches. The shoots have restored, so far as possible, the normal pattern of growth.

A more drastic experiment is to cut off the main leader itself. One or more of the laterals below it will then bend upward to replace the loss. There is often a competition for the leader's post—like the competition for power when a dictator dies—the winner being the one that is stoutest and quickest to move; the rest drop back to their secondary role. Sometimes the contest is indecisive; two branches share the leadership, and a forked trunk results.

Many similar experiments can be performed by the ingenious distorter of nature—such as tying the leader into a loop, bending the laterals in a horizontal plane so that they do not grow directly out from the trunk, and so on. The upshot of all these is proof of the persistent tendency of the growing portions of the tree to restore their normal relation to the rest, their typical position in the pattern of the whole. How they react depends upon their situation. A terminal shoot behaves differently from a lateral one, and a lateral leader behaves differently from its own secondary laterals.

How, we may ask, are these differences in position brought about? If you cut off a lateral branch of a pine or any other coniferous tree, you will find on the lower side of it a triangular segment, occupying one-fourth to one-third of the whole, that is reddish in color. This is what the foresters call "reaction wood." Its cells are shorter and more numerous than are the cells in normal wood, and in growing it tends to expand lengthwise a little. Its presence on the underside of a branch thus holds the branch up and balances the downward pull of gravity. Whichever side of an axis forms reaction wood will tend to become a little longer than the other, and the axis will bend away from this side. When a lateral branch is artificially pulled upward, the bending of its free portion back downward to a normal position again is due to the development of reaction wood on the upper (inner) side. When the normal direction is restored, this wood is no longer formed on the upper side but now appears on the lower, thus checking the downward movement and holding the branch against the pull of gravity. When a leader is cut off, reaction wood develops in abundance on the lower side of the base of each lateral below it, pushing it up toward the vertical position. Reaction wood is absent from vertical shoots and thus from the main trunk of the trees—a fortunate fact, since the structural properties of this wood make it inferior for lumber. Occasionally when trunks have been tipped partly over, as by a windstorm, reaction wood, developing on their lower sides, has been known to bend them back to a vertical position again, even when they were six inches or more in diameter—a task requiring tremendous growth pressure. The significant thing is that in every case reaction wood is the agent by which these regulatory movements of stem and branches are brought about.

In many other trees similar growth movements bring structures back to their normal orientation. The tissues that do this, however, since they are not distinguishable by their color as is the reaction wood of conifers, are not so readily observed.

But, you may say, this is only part of the answer. What makes reaction wood develop? There is good evidence that it is formed by the characteristic plant growth hormone *auxin,* by which the movements of the softer parts of plants toward or away from the direction of light or gravity is determined. This is about as far as the plant physiologist can go at present toward an explanation of these regulatory movements in the pine and similar plants, but it is obviously not far enough. The various parts of the tree form an angular pattern with one another, which is characteristic for the species. It is this particular pattern that reaction wood restores by gently pushing the erring member back to where it belongs and holding it there. This fact, simple though its statement and demonstration may be, has profound implications, for it poses the question of why just enough reaction wood—and thus just enough auxin—is produced at just the right place and at just the proper time to maintain or restore the typical form of the tree. Implanted in the living stuff of the white pine, in its inherited genetic constitution, is the tendency to develop just this pattern and to maintain it by a constant monitorship that restores it if it is disturbed. The pine tree, simple though it is in comparison with the higher animals, is, like them, an *organized, self-regulating system* with a specific type of structure implanted in it. As to just how this structure is developed and maintained, biology is almost without a clue. The pine in the old pasture, like the flower in the crannied wall, poses some problems that reach down to the very foundations of life. If we knew what makes a pine grow from a pine seed, and stay precisely a pine through all the vicissitudes of its history, we should come close to knowing what life really is.

New Plants from Old

In the days when almost every housewife had geraniums blossoming through the winter in her south windows, there came a time in spring when the plants had grown too tall and "leggy" to be attractive any longer. Before throwing them out she started from them a new lot of "slips." The process is simple and familiar. With a sharp knife the tip of a vigorous young shoot was cut off, and the base of it was put into water or damp sand. Before many days a circle of root tips began to appear at the cut end, and soon a well-rooted plant became established. A dozen such might thus be grown from one old plant—its offspring by this simple, sexless process of vegetative propagation. Each was a piece of its parent, removed from a subordinate position as part of a larger whole and now, by the growth of its own roots, restoring a new whole again. These small plants, when they reached full size, might be cut up to form more new ones, and these in turn might produce still others through a series that can be indefinitely prolonged. By such multiplication many kinds of plants are propagated in our greenhouses and gardens. The art of rooting cuttings reaches back to the dawn of horticulture and was known even before Theophrastus, the father of botany, practiced it in Aristotle's well-stocked Athenian garden many centuries ago.

Unlike plants grown from seeds, which are the results of sexual mixing and scrambling of traits, such vegetative offspring are rigidly true to type since each is a part, though many times removed, of its first ancestor. All the Concord grapevines in the world are far-flung pieces of that promising seedling Ephraim Bull nurtured so carefully in his

Concord garden more than a century ago. Every Burbank potato, likewise, is a faithful replica of the potatoes borne by the plant which the immortal Luther, with his uncanny power to distinguish the superior from the commonplace, had selected among hundreds growing on his old farm in Lunenburg.

So far as we can tell, such a perennially propagated group of plants, all members one of another, can live forever. Its youthful vigor is renewed each time a shoot is set apart as a new individual. The decrepitude of age cannot affect it as a whole. Cuttings from the ancient Washington elm, taken before it finally toppled over in the fullness of its years, made trees as vigorous and youthful as their parent must have been two centuries before. Senescence seems not to be inevitable in plants like this. It is the price that highly developed organisms like ourselves must pay for their complexity. Life at a lower level is potentially immortal.

The most significant fact, however, about such vegetative multiplying is that a piece of a plant removed from its stock will restore the parts it lacks and thus become a complete whole again. All is in balance. Roots on a cutting do not grow indefinitely but only until the normal ratio of root to shoot has been restored. Somehow in this little budding tip there is in miniature the making of the whole, but this capacity is never manifest unless the tip is isolated from the rest. What it will do depends on where it is, but ever and persistently the outcome is not a heterogeneous medley of leaves and stems and roots but a series of orderly *whole plants*. As every soldier in Napoleon's army carried the potential baton of a marshal in his knapsack, so each branch of a geranium carries the possibility of a whole plant in itself.

Not only roots but many other parts may be restored. Consider a young bean plant, pushing up out of the soil and lifting its shriveled seed-leaves into the air. From between them grows the young green shoot with its bud and its first pair of leaves. If all goes well the bean plant develops normally from this, but if you cut off this shoot the career of the young vegetable is by no means ended. At the base of each seed-leaf, in the angle between it and the stem, there is a tiny bud. These usually remain quite dormant, but if the main shoot is removed, one or both of them begin to grow and soon restore the parts that have been lost. By one way or another the bean is bound to reach its goal of a whole plant.

In these cases restoration of a missing part follows its actual physical removal. The same things happen if the part is functionally isolated from the rest, even though still in contact with it. In the bean seedling, for example, one may chill a bit of the young stem above the seed-leaves by circling it with a coil containing ice water. This does not kill it but does bring to a halt the life activities in this region and effectually isolates it from the rest of the young plant below. The dormant buds now spring into growth just as though the shoot above them had been quite cut off.

In all these cases, as in the pine seedling, the chief chemical agent that is concerned is known—the growth hormone, auxin. Its presence in the young terminal bud prevents the development of buds below it, and this same mechanism is effective in controlling bud and branch development throughout the plant; but, as in other cases, the difficulty lies not in identifying the "chemical messenger" involved but the controlling factor that determines its amount and the time and place of its operation.

The regeneration of whole plants from small parts that

have been isolated becomes more remarkable when one observes the precise way in which it is accomplished. How roots and shoots grow from a cutting is by no means a hit-or-miss affair. If one cuts off a willow twig in spring and wraps it in damp sphagnum moss, roots will sprout from it, and buds will swell and grow. The roots, however, come chiefly from the bottom of the twig, the end that was cut off from the parent tree, and the buds that push out are the ones at the other end. This is the effect of gravity, you may say; but try keeping the willow twig upside down while it is sprouting, and you will find it makes no difference. Roots still grow out from what was once the lower (now the upper) end, and shoots at the other. The twig still has the same root end and shoot end. We may cut it into smaller and smaller pieces, and each will show this same two-endedness. It reminds one of the two poles of a magnetic needle. This polarity may well extend to the minute cells of which the plant is built; each may have its root end and its shoot end, and the qualities of these ends finally come to expression in the orderly two-ended system of the plant that grows from the regenerating twig.

Such restoration of missing parts in plants is familiar to everyone whose thumb is green or who has watched the work of gardeners. All this is "natural," we are apt to think; but we forget how remarkable it really is that the little cutting so regulates its growth and its activities that the outcome always tends to be a perfect, balanced whole. Just as the pine sapling persistently restores its normal growth pattern when this is forcibly altered by the constraint of bonds, so do most plants tend to restore their patterns when they are more drastically changed by the removal of parts. Somehow, we repeat, there must be present in the plant's living stuff, immanent in all its parts, something that represents the natural configuration of the whole, as a norm to which its growth conforms, a "goal" toward which development is invariably directed. This insistent fact confronts us everywhere in biology.

Growth Keeps in Step

Of all the kinds of plants that gardeners grow, the common gourd has the widest range of variation. Its species is called *Cucurbita Pepo* by the botanist. To this protean group belong the summer squashes—crook-necks, straightnecks, patty-pans, cymlings, cocozelles, and all the rest; the pumpkins, big and little; and a host of ornamental gourds of almost every color, size, and form. Another species in the same family, *Lagenaria siceraria,* is almost as versatile, for it includes the bottle gourds, large and small; the long club gourds; the sugar troughs, calabashes, jugs, and many others. Gourd growers collect the fruits of both these species as some people do postage stamps. The various forms within each may be hybridized with ease. One can scramble and unscramble them to his heart's content and, if he so inclines, can find in his experiments new examples of the famous laws of heredity that Gregor Mendel discovered in his cloister garden long ago. The gourds our grandfathers once used as dippers, jugs, and nest eggs are grown in more abundance now than ever, but for pleasure, not for practicality.

Though fruit shapes in these species are widely varied, the fruits on a single plant are all alike. Each shape is inherited, determined by specific genetic factors. This does not strike us as remarkable, for we are used to the fact that like begets like and would be shocked indeed to find a pumpkin vine that bore tomatoes. And yet the production of a gourd fruit, true at every stage to its hereditary type, is one of those biological marvels that become the more remarkable as we study them closely.

The young fruit starts out as a minute mass of cells about as big as the point of a pin, the ovary rudiment of a tiny female flower. From this comes the fully developed ovary, and then, after fertilization occurs, the fruit itself. Something far more subtle than mere expansion is happening here. At every step of its development the growing structure has a precise form, and this form slowly changes as it grows. All types are alike at the very earliest stage—tiny, rounded groups of cells, and that is all. Very soon, when the young ovary is barely visible to the naked eye, its characteristic shape begins to be distinguishable. Each particular shape is the result of growth that is more rapid in certain dimensions than in others. The patient observer who carefully measures the growing ovaries at successive stages can see this form unfolding day by day. It changes slowly but steadily until maturity.

If you examine the growing ovary of a bottle gourd, for example, you will find that as it enlarges it becomes relatively wider; the width increases faster than the length, so that the larger the fruit grows the more squat its outline is. The remarkable fact about this is that the ratio of the growth rate in length to the growth rate in width is constant. In this particular type, length grows only about eighty per cent as fast as width. The actual rate of either growth, in terms of millimeters per day, is by no means constant, for it is slow at first, then increasingly fast, and finally slow again until it stops entirely when the fruit reaches its mature size. What is constant is the *relative* rate of growth in each dimension as compared to all the others. Whether fast or slow, each growth rate keeps step with all the rest. At whatever pace the metronome of growth beats, each dimension—not length and width alone—increases in a strict proportion to its fellows, and the pattern of the whole is slowly altered.

In different types this pattern changes differently. Though in the bottle gourd width grows more rapidly than length, in the club type the reverse is true, so that here the fruit becomes not fatter as it grows but more elongated. In the rounded ones both dimensions grow at about the same rates, and here the early form persists with little change until the end.

How, one may ask, are these differences in growth rate brought about? What happens in the protoplasmic recesses of the plant to make one dimension increase faster than another and in due proportion? Here the microscope provides a partial answer. The growing gourd fruit, like every other plant or animal body, is formed of millions of tiny living units tightly packed—the cells, which can be seen only when highly magnified. Most growth is due not to a progressive swelling of these cells but to an increase in the number of them. This happens by the division of each into two daughter cells, which then increase to the size their mother was. Each then divides again into two more, and so on and on.

Cell division takes place in a rather complex fashion, the details of which need not concern us here. Before division each cell, as one sees it in section, is about as broad as it is long. Its central kernel, the nucleus, first divides into two new ones by a process which insures that the threadlike chromosomes—important because they contain the essential directive units or genes—are apportioned equally to the two daughter nuclei. Between the two nuclei there appears a delicate membrane, stretching across the cell and dividing it into two. Each daughter cell, now about half as wide as it is long, expands until the two dimensions are the same. Size thus has doubled, but the *direction* of this size increase is determined by the plane in which the nucleus divides, for this decides the position of the partition wall and thus the direction in which the expansion of the daughter cells occurs. If the cells divide more frequently in one plane than in another, growth will be more rapid at right angles to that plane. The decisive event in determining the direction of growth seems to be the plane of division. In the undivided, roundish cell with its nucleus in the center there is usually no hint as to what this direction will be when the cell next divides. Something—and here is the nub of the matter—decides which of all the various planes of division open to it will actually be chosen. If the teeming millions of cells divided at random and in all directions, growth would be equal everywhere, and a more or less spherical structure would result, something that often happens in galls and tumors. If division is most frequent in one plane, growth will be faster in one direction than in the others.

That this is true can be shown by studying young, growing ovaries that are to make fruits of different forms. If one looks through the microscope at a thin lengthwise slice of one of these, he can see cells in the process of division, and in each he can measure the angle that the plane of division makes with the long axis of the fruit—the line from the stalk to the tip of the young bud. By taking a census of hundreds of such divisions in a given race, he can then count the frequency of the various divisional planes. In the snake gourd, for example, the observer finds that almost all of these are at right angles to the axis of the ovary and only a few of them are parallel to it. Thus, as the

daughter cells expand they tend to make the ovary grow
in length much faster than in width, so that the characteristic snakelike form results. In broad, flat types of gourds,
on the contrary, lengthwise divisions are more numerous,
and growth in width is thus more rapid.

In most types of gourd, however, conditions are not so
simple as this, for divisions are taking place in almost all
directions. To look at a thin slice of a young gourd ovary
(and the same would be true of almost any bit of young
plant tissue) is to behold what looks like the utmost confusion. Some cells are dividing parallel to the axis, some at
right angles to it, and most at other angles. Many cells have
not been able to assume a rounded form because of growth
pressures exerted by their neighbors. Here seems to be a
cellular rabble, a chaos of indecision that must surely lead
to formlessness. But actually this is far removed from chaos.
It is a small cosmos of the most orderly behavior, for if one
observes the little ovary expanding, he sees it proceed
along a perfectly regular course. In one case width grows
a little faster than does length. Projecting ribs appear along
the sides. The base of the ovary narrows to a neck, and
other parts of a specific, developing pattern begin to appear.

To me there are few sights in nature more impressive
than this demonstration of an orderly control exercised
over what seems to be a disorderly tangle of dividing cells
apparently growing at cross purposes. Something inherent
in the entire mass, something residing in its fundamental
genetic constitution, keeps it marching steadily forward to
a precise culmination. The nature of this "something" that
coordinates the multifarious activities of growth into a
harmonious system, that directs them on a steady course,
is the greatest unsolved problem of biology. It underlies

all the examples we have been discussing. Form is characteristic of living things because it is the visible expression of this orderly organic control, this deep, goal-seeking directiveness.

Scrambled Sponges

A mystifying trick with which a conjurer delights to fool his audience is to take a paper handkerchief, present it to us in its pristine and unwrinkled state, tear it ostentatiously into little bits, jam these together tightly into a wad, and then loosen this same twisted mass and spread it out before our wondering eyes as an untorn handkerchief, miraculously whole again. What amazes us is not any magical restoration, for common sense assures us this can never happen, but rather the conjurer's skill in substituting a new handkerchief for the torn fragments of the old.

But common sense may sometimes be mistaken. Actually a restoration very much like this can happen in the cold light of the laboratory, where a living organism, the magician of nature, confronts us with facts still more bizarre. Consider, for example, the story of the scrambled sponge.

Half a century ago an imaginative biologist, Professor H. V. Wilson, studying sponges at a seaside laboratory, performed an experiment simple enough in nature but so astonishing in its implications that it has become a classic in zoology. Sponges are widely varied in character. The familiar ones, which are dedicated to the bath or other cleansing processes, are simply the skeletons of the larger and more complex kinds from which all living tissue has carefully been removed. In the sponge as it grows in nature, the surfaces of this skeleton, inside and out, are covered with layers of living cells. Sponges are simple animals. They have no typical sense organs or muscles or stomachs such as are found in the higher forms of life. Some of them are hardly more than cellular colonies. They are far more complex, however, than single-celled animals like the amoeba, and in them are the beginnings of that organized division of labor that finally makes possible a complex animal like man.

The basic plan of a sponge is a tubular structure into which water is drawn through a multitude of tiny pores, passed along a canal or series of canals, and then forced out of a vent. This is accomplished by thousands of tiny cells that line the canals. Each cell has a little collar and within this a threadlike whip which is waved back and forth, more vigorously toward the vent than in the other direction, and thus draws water in and wafts it along. From this stream of water, as it passes by them, the cells absorb whatever minute bits of food it may contain. In addition to the collar cells there are several other kinds—the ones that compose the skin or epidermis, the ones of the middle layer, and the ones that form the tough skeleton by which the soft body of the sponge is supported.

Some sponges have definite bodily forms, but in others the form is rather irregular. All, however, develop the typical cellular organization by which water is kept flowing through the whole. The species on which most of Professor Wilson's experiments were performed belongs to the genus *Microciona,* which makes bright red crustlike masses on the surfaces of stones and other objects covered by shallow water near the shore. The surface of this species is usually thrust up into irregular, thickish lobes.

Most sponges are able to produce new individuals by a process of regeneration, from pieces cut out of the old sponge. This is not surprising, since many simple animals can do so. But just how much cutting up will a sponge stand

and still be able to reproduce a normal individual? No one, apparently, had tried to find an answer to this question before Professor Wilson undertook to do so. To break up the sponge as completely as possible without killing it, he first tried to pull it apart with needles. This was not thorough enough, so instead he subjected it to the most drastic physical mauling any living organism could face—he squeezed it through the tiny pores of fine-meshed bolting cloth. About a gram of clean, fresh sponge tissue was placed in a small cloth bag under water and gently jammed together with forceps. The structure of the sponge was thoroughly mashed by this treatment, and the softer portions were pushed out through the cloth's tiny pores. The sieve was so fine that to pass it the tissue had to be broken up into single cells or very small groups of cells. As they came through the bottom of the bag these thousands of minute bits, falling through the water down to the surface of a glass plate, looked like a small, reddish cloud. Surely this was the ultimate in the disintegration of an organism. What expectation could there be that a living thing, its delicate fabric thus so completely disorganized and its tiny cells all rent asunder, could survive?

But a sponge turns out to be an unexpectedly tough animal. Though its delicate structure may be thus drastically disintegrated, the cells that compose it, if the operation is skillfully done, come through alive. They are not closely held together as a plant's cells or those of a higher animal are, and thus slip apart rather easily. When they fall through the water to the plate under the filter bag, most of the cells, now free, begin to behave like tiny amoebae, gliding over the surface and sending out questing protoplasmic strands or filaments. Now comes the most remarkable part of the story. These minute individuals, released from the bonds that once held them together in this simple cellular society, seem not to cherish their newly found independence. When two approach each other and their filaments touch, the cells promptly fuse. The two fused cells in turn soon add a third to their company, and then another and another, until the host of separate cells, simple in character and all much alike, have come together into small roundish masses. All remaining stray cells are soon incorporated into nearby groups. Adjacent masses now fuse, and finally the whole body of cells, once completely separated, may produce a few large groups or even a single one, which finally forms a crust on the surface of the slide. As a school of fish or a flock of birds, scattered by the attack of an enemy, will mobilize into a compact group again, so these disunited cells, in a few hours or days, pull themselves together to form something not unlike the original body of which they all once were members. Soon in this mass the characteristic cellular differences appear—an outer epidermal layer, middle tissue, skeletal cells, and canals with their surfaces covered by collar cells and beating whips.

Whether, as the result of their drastic separation, all the cells revert to a primitive embryonic form from which any type of cell may later arise in the new sponge, or whether some of them may keep their original characters and assume their proper places once again, is not certain, but the new whole is built by the spontaneous assembling of individual units, each of which develops into a cell characteristic for the particular place it happens to occupy. These cells do not come together to form a disorganized throng such as one sees in certain kinds of abnormal plant or animal growth or in cultures of various tissues; but, like soldiers in a well-drilled military unit, when the bugle blows they assemble in orderly formation. In some way the structure of the whole sponge, with its specific pattern and its cellular variety, is immanent in each individual cell. How this is possible is a secret still locked in the innermost structure of protoplasm. Evidently each tiny living unit is a much more complex thing than it appears to be, for it bears within itself an image of the whole organism, the "goal" toward which its development persistently will move.

The Slime Mold and Its Culture Pattern

In an obscure family of very simple plants there occurs naturally a developmental process not unlike the one artificially produced by Professor Wilson in his experiment with the sponges. The story is among the most remarkable in biological literature.

Slime molds are almost the simplest of living things. Their bodies are naked masses of protoplasm not unlike the body of the familiar amoeba of the biological laboratory. Their claim to be regarded as plants comes from the fact that they reproduce by airborne spores, as do most fungi. They probably should be regarded as members of neither the animal nor the plant kingdom but as belonging to that somewhat nebulous group of organisms that stand part way between plants and animals.

Most slime molds consist of a single mass of protoplasm, containing many nuclei but not divided into separate cells. They live on decaying logs and in similar situations, and sometimes reach considerable size, though they never become conspicuous. One small group, however, so insignificant as to be without a "common" name and to be designated only by its technical family name of *Acrasiaceae*, differs from typical slime molds in a number of ways. The individual here is not a substantial mass of protoplasm but a tiny cell so small that it cannot be seen without a rather high magnification by the microscope. It has no wall, and creeps about in its damp environment much like a miniature amoeba (indeed, it is called a *myxamoeba*), seeking the still smaller bacteria that are its food. It multiplies by the simple process of dividing itself in two, and is limited in numbers only by the amount of food available.

After a time a change comes over the swarming mass of these tiny separate cellular individuals. Either food begins to fail or, as some recent work suggests, here and there two myxamoebae fuse in a sort of sexual union. At all events, feeding and multiplication cease, and the cells begin to move toward a center. If one grows the cells on the surface of agar jelly he can see these aggregations plainly, even with the naked eye. When the process is speeded up to our vision by fast-run motion pictures, the cells seem to stream in toward one of these centers like people running to a fire, following converging lines or paths, and almost treading on each other's heels. What makes them do this is not clearly known, but the production of a specific chemical substance attractive to the cells seems to be one of the factors.

When a great number of them—from ten thousand to fifty thousand individuals, usually—have thus come together, migration finally ceases. Each of the thousands of cells milling about in this seething mass keeps its identity and does not fuse with any of the others. Here, one might confidently say, is an undisciplined, swarming mob of independent cells. But such is not the case. In this little cellular republic in which, so far as we can see, every citizen is like every other one, remarkable events now begin to take place. Discipline is established. The mass pulls itself together into a lumpish, elongate structure (technically called a *pseudoplasmodium*), about two millimeters long and about the size of a birdseed. By a kind of gliding motion, still not well understood, this mass now slowly moves toward a lighter, dryer spot more favorable for spore production. It looks somewhat like an undulating, chubby worm, its forward tip lifted a little above the surface on which it moves. This tip is the directive center of the whole and seems to organize the swarm of individual cells into a system. If it is removed the plasmodium is confused and stops. When, by a delicate operation, the tip is cut off and then placed against the side of another mass, it will start there an independence movement, so to speak, draw under its control a group of cells, pull them away from their former comrades, and march off at the head of a new body.

The two ends of the axis of this cellular society are quite different, and only the "head" end has this organizing power. The other end follows, but never leads. This little swarm of gliding individuals is thus not a mob but a cellular state and shows the beginnings of that organized diversity which in higher plants and animals makes an organism.

But the most remarkable behavior is yet to come. This migrating plasmodium finally stops moving and settles down into a roundish mass something like a small biscuit. The individual cells on the lowest tier, which are touching the surface over which they have been moving, now anchor themselves firmly to it and form a little disk, strong enough to hold the structure that is to be built. Meanwhile, the cells along the vertical axis of the mass become thick-walled and stick together, forming a solid stalk. This grows at its upper end by the continual dedication of more cells to its formation. The great body of individuals, still free and uncommitted, glide over one another and somehow clamber up this stalk as it grows until they finally form a spherical mass at its tip. The whole now looks a bit like a small, round-headed pin. Each cell in this mass rounds up to form a dark spore, and these thousands of spores dry out and are blown away, each to produce a new amoeba-like individual.

This remarkable behavior has excited the interest of botanists ever since it was discovered. In another type of slime molds, the spore-bearing structure is still more complex, for besides a single spore-case at the top there are also several whorls of spore-cases along the stalk, each borne at the tip of a small side branch.

There are a number of kinds of these molds. On the basis of the form and other characteristics of its fruiting body each is given a technical name, both genus and species, as in higher plants. The type we have here described is *Dictyostelium discoideum*. If amoebae that come from different types—but which look exactly alike—are mixed together by an experimenter they will form a migrating cell mass. When the time comes for this to produce a spore-bearing structure, however, the two types of individuals tend to sort themselves out and finally to make fruiting structures characteristic of the types from which they came.

How such a beautifully coordinated body as this can be produced by a swarming mass of cells, gliding over one another, each apparently a freely moving individual, is very difficult to explain. The size of the final fruiting body depends on the number of individuals that came together in the aggregating mass, and the size of the disk and the thickness of the stalk are adjusted to the mechanical strain that is imposed on them. Recent experiment has shown that in some types the aggregating mass may be very small, sometimes consisting of as few as twenty-eight cells. Even in its tiny fruiting structure the form of the whole is reproduced in miniature. About a dozen cells make the disk; three, end to end, the stalk, and the rest the mass of spores.

Every amoeboid cell looks like every other one and apparently shares all the same chemical and physical characteristics. In each, however, there must be some sort of directiveness which, when the group is mobilized, produces by complex intercellular adjustments a specific structure. The potentialities for building this structure must in some way be inherent in each cell, though what the mechanism is by which it operates we have not yet the faintest idea. This case is even more remarkable than that of the scrambled sponge cells, for here the cells are not artificially pulled apart but are separate from the first. This little cellular society seems to have a set of very precise regulations which each individual faithfully obeys, but how each finds what its particular task is to be eludes us. More plainly than elsewhere, we are faced here with the fact that among completely similar protoplasmic units differences arise that in time lead to the formation of a very precisely organized system. The character of this organism must in some way be prefigured in the living cells from which it grew. Here is the essence of biological organization.

Metamorphosis

Many events in the life histories of animals have excited men's wonder through the centuries—how from an egg a fledgling is hatched out, how birds and fish can migrate so unerringly across the wastes of air and sea, how bees and ants maintain complex societies—but none, perhaps, has so stirred our imagination as has the amazing way in which

a humble, crawling, earth-bound caterpillar, after its chrys-
alis sleep, becomes transformed into a moth or butterfly.
Children with wide eyes have watched it happen, poets
have sung of it, and preachers have compared it to the
death and resurrection of the body. The contrast between
these two creatures is so great, and the inert cocoon into
which one disappears and from which the other emerges is
so seemingly lifeless, that these events have always appealed
to men's sense of mystery. Here indeed is a miracle of transformation as amazing as any that was ever brought to pass
by the waving of a fairy's wand or a magician's incanta-
tion.

And the process is, indeed, almost miraculous. The egg of
a silkworm, for example, hatches into a small grub, and
this in turn grows to be a voracious caterpillar, consuming
many times its weight in mulberry leaves. When its full size
—about three inches long—is reached, the caterpillar ends
its feast, and a change comes over its behavior. It raises its
head and begins to sway gently back and forth. Soon from a
spinneret in its lower lip emerges a tiny silken strand
which the caterpillar fastens to a twig or other firm support.
Weaving around and around for several days in wide figure
eights, it slowly constructs a mantle about itself, a thousand
yards or more of precious silk, until it is tightly bound
within a white cocoon.

Then all is quiet, and the caterpillar seems to have fallen
asleep, wrapped in a silken shroud. Sleep of a sort this
might perhaps be called, but within its body the little animal now begins a transformation of the most fantastic sort,
for many of its organs and tissues are scrapped and discarded, and from their substance an entirely different set
of structures—the organs of the winged moth—is now de-

veloped. It is as though this organism were two different animals, the second created from the bodily debris of the first.

How these changes come about we do not understand, though hormone action of various sorts is evidently involved. The first problem is to find how the organs of the caterpillar are broken down. This is no process of decay such as would happen if the body died and decomposed. And yet something not unlike this actually does occur. In the bloodstream of the caterpillar, as in our own bloodstreams, there is a host of phagocytes, a special type of white blood corpuscle whose function it is to act as scavengers by absorbing foreign material and especially by devouring harmful bacteria, thus preventing serious infection. To such efficient police work many organisms owe their relative freedom from bacterial attack. Within the quiescent caterpillar, however, these phagocytes perform a very different task, for they now turn upon the body they have been protecting and devour and disintegrate many of its tissues. The muscles, the intestinal tract, the large salivary glands, and the skin itself are thus destroyed. Other parts break down by enzyme action. In the end, almost all of the original internal structures of the caterpillar, save for a part of the heart and nervous system, have disappeared.

This is no sudden onslaught but a gradual process, and it is accompanied from the start by the growth of new organs. Now appears a strange sort of embryology. Even in the body of the caterpillar there are present here and there tiny disk-like islands of embryonic tissue, the so-called "imaginal disks," which simply bide their time until the hour arrives for them to take their parts in the drama of regeneration. Some are in the head, others in the tissues under the skin, and still others in the walls of the intestine. They are immune to phagocyte attack, and as soon as the degeneration of the old structures begins they develop into active centers of growth from which the new structures are gradually formed. The process of transformation is an orderly one; the second set of organs, step by step, replaces the first. A new set of mouth parts, suitable for the very different kind of food the moth will eat, is formed. Two pairs of wings develop, beautifully folded together and packed into the narrow space inside the cocoon, ready to expand when the moth emerges, and to carry it in its new environment. Sexual organs are developed, for the chief function of this stage in the animal's life is to produce male and female sex cells through the union of which a new generation of grubs and caterpillars will come.

After several weeks the growth of the new structures is complete, and the cocoon is filled with quite a different animal from the one that made it—a white moth. This second edition of the organism is radically different from the first. It is made from the same material, for practically nothing has entered or left the cocoon since it was formed; but the entire bodily architecture has been altered. Just as a new house is sometimes built from the materials of an older one, so the new moth is a complete reconstruction of the substance of the caterpillar.

This is perhaps no more remarkable than ordinary development, for the tiny disks from which the body of the moth develops are really bits of embryonic stuff. Just as the form of the caterpillar was present, so to speak, in the constitution of the egg from which it grew, so the structure of the moth is in some way prefigured in the series of disks from which its parts develop. The process here is more complex than in a normal embryonic history, for here the body is formed not from a single egg but by simultaneous development from a group of separate centers. Coordination of some sort must exist between them in this beautifully integrated program of growth, where every process takes its proper place and a single whole animal is formed by the cooperation of many separate groups of cells. This is regeneration, but regeneration of a most unusual sort.

In insects with such a life history, therefore, there is not simply a single developmental goal, such as is present in most embryos, but a double one. The technical word that describes this most remarkable process is well chosen, a *metamorphosis,* and such it is indeed.

The Resourceful Embryo

Most of us have gathered in the spring the eggs of frogs or toads—members of that great group of animals that are at home in water and on land and thus are well named amphibians. Their egg masses are handfuls of gray jelly deposited by the female in a quiet pond or pool. Scattered through the jelly are small dark dots about the size of birdshot—the eggs themselves. They have been fertilized and are already beginning to develop. Since they are relatively large and not encased in hard shells, they provide favorite objects of study for young embryologists.

And they well repay such study. Step by step, the embryo marches on in its development. The egg is first cut in two by a partition wall down the middle. Another wall, at right angles to the first, divides these cells in turn, and the four are arranged like the quarters of an apple. Each cell now divides crosswise, so that a group of eight is formed. This process of cleavage continues until hundreds of cells have been produced, but it is more rapid, and the cells are thus smaller, on the upper side of the young embryonic mass. The larger cells below are filled with yolk substance. This solid mass of cells now pulls apart in the center to make a hollow sphere. Part way down its side there next appears a dimple on the surface, which rapidly becomes deeper, pushing the outer layer into the middle of the hollow. It thus obliterates most of the original cavity and forms a new one, which will in time become the digestive tract. The small opening to the outside, the original dimple, is destined to be the posterior end of this, and at the other end a second opening now pushes through to the outside to make the primitive mouth. On the upper surface two puckered folds appear, which mark the position of the future vertebral axis. These folds grow over and meet to enclose the neural tube, where the spinal cord will lie. Gill slits appear on the sides of the embryo, near the mouth. Buds of the limbs push out and form the forelegs and the hind legs. Eyes soon develop. The embryo is drawn out sharply at the rear to form a tail. These outer changes are accompanied by a development of the inner organs and their complex tissues, until finally the tadpole frees itself and swims away.

This process, which may take several weeks in nature, gains in dramatic impact if we watch it when it is speeded up by time-lapse motion pictures. We can watch the egg as it is cleft, dimpled, puckered, and molded into the tadpole, for all the world as if the unseen hands of a craftsman were shaping it. What takes place here is no simple enlargement, no mere swelling. It is an unfolding, a development; each part is in step with all the rest, some marking time, and others moving on more rapidly. In this humble history one sees the consummation of a very specific developmental program, the course of which must be foreshadowed in the egg cell from which the whole has come. In the deceptively simple-looking substance of this egg there is a highly organized living system, which in some way prefigures the various steps in embryonic history: first the tadpole, and finally, gills and tail sloughed off, the adult toad or frog. Development moves indomitably on as if to a final goal.

Such, with no very radical differences, is the embryonic history of all vertebrates. In the lower groups of animals and in plants there are simpler developmental programs, but they are no less definitely directed toward the final production of an organism of a very precise kind. How to explain this sure-footed embryonic march from egg to adult is the question that makes the science of embryology so difficult—and so fascinating.

But if normal embryology is hard to understand, what shall we say of those remarkable cases where its course is disturbed experimentally but where it still proceeds persistently toward its normal goal? If the first two cells into which the egg of an amphibian divides are separated from each other, each rounds itself up into an egglike cell of half the usual size. After such drastic treatment we might expect these cells to die, or at best to make half-embryos. Astonishingly enough, this is not what happens. Each cell, undismayed, acts as if it were an egg and proceeds to go through the normal steps of embryology and to form a tadpole. Evidently each of these two cells has the potentialities within itself to form a whole animal. So long as it was joined to its sister cell, however, it did not call these forth but played its proper part in a single whole. It was this remarkable behavior that persuaded Driesch that the organism could not be a simple physical mechanism, for such, he thought, would not be capable of being divided into pieces each of which could then remake a whole. There is much further evidence now, especially from plants, that every cell of an organism has within it the potentiality to make a whole, though this rarely can be realized after the cell has progressed beyond its early stages. While it still possesses this potentiality, however, it does not exercise it but subordinates itself to the developing pattern which the whole mass of cells is forming, and takes its proper place within it. What it will become depends on where it is.

The same tendency to move toward a single whole is shown in other ways. Techniques are at hand by the use of which two eggs may be fused to form a single cell—just the reverse of the process we have been describing. Here, however, instead of two embryos, only one is formed. Any continuous mass of living stuff tends to make a single organism, and it will do this despite formidable difficulties. If the first few cells of a developing embryo, for example, are kept between two glass plates, they are forced to form a flattened mass of cells quite different from the normal, rounded one. When pressure is removed, however, these cells reorganize their disrupted system and go on to form a normal whole.

And it is a complete whole that tends so persistently to be produced, despite attempts to alter it. The developing amphibian is excellent material in which to study the processes of regeneration. If a young gill or leg or tail is snipped off, a group of actively dividing cells arises at its stump and slowly reconstructs the missing part. Such restoration takes place only in the tadpole stage, but it is a notable example of the powerful tendency of any organized living system to complete itself.

"The fate of a cell," said Driesch, "is a function of its position"—its position in the whole toward which, as toward a goal, embryonic development persistently is moving. That is what biological organization really means.

The developmental histories that have been recounted here illustrate the remarkable quality of living things by which their bodily growth is so controlled that it moves persistently toward the production of a single, whole organism, characteristic in size and form. Its growth is regulated in conformity to a norm. The final goal toward which it moves —the form of the mature individual—and the several steps through which it will be reached, seem in some way immanent in all its diverse parts. One is reminded of von Bertalanffy's remark that as a storage battery is charged with electricity, so is a fertilized egg charged with form. Instances of such developmental self-regulation could be drawn from the life histories of almost every sort of animal and plant. It is universal in biology. The purpose of discussing these examples has been to emphasize this basic fact, for in much biological teaching it is lost in the enumeration of details about life processes. It is this *directiveness* that is the most distinctive feature of a living thing. Protoplasm does not make formless structures; it builds *organisms*. In this fact there resides, I think, a clue for the reconciliation of the two parts of man's dual nature.

CHAPTER III

Protoplasm and Purpose

Abstract

An organism, as it develops from an egg or seed, so regulates its growth that it moves steadily on to the production of a mature individual of a very definite kind. A similar directiveness and self-regulation is evident in behavior, and thus in mental traits. The suggestion is offered that this tendency toward goal-seeking, manifest in the activities of both body and mind, is a basic characteristic of *all* life, and that life is thus inherently goal-directed and purposeful. As the traits of a mature individual are immanent in the egg from which it will develop, so a purpose, yet to be realized, may be said to be immanent in the cells of the brain. Mental activity is far more varied and complex than bodily development, but both are rooted in the self-regulating and goal-seeking nature of protoplasm. All ideas at first were purposes. This concept interprets body and mind not as two unlike things but as two aspects of a fundamental unity.

Several objections can be raised against this hypothesis: 1. Goal-seeking implies the effective operation of purpose, which seems to violate the uniformity of nature and imply a "final" cause. Especially does it oppose the psychological concept of "drive" by substituting for it an inner directive. 2. The difference

49

between the regulation of bodily development and a conscious mental process is so very great that it is difficult to regard them as fundamentally alike. 3. It is hard to see how the rich and constantly changing stream of mental life in man could have come from the single-track directiveness of an embryological process. Answers to these objections are presented in some detail.

If this conception is sound, a study of developmental processes in the laboratory may throw light on the nature of mental processes and bring biology and psychology—and thus body and mind—more closely together.

These examples of the coordination and regulation living things display in their growth, development, and activity illustrate the basic fact of biological organization. A plant or an animal is an organized system, a single whole organism, in which each part and activity is closely correlated with all the rest. Throughout its life this living system maintains itself against the disorganizing tendencies in lifeless matter, which begin at once to break the system down as soon as death occurs. The process of development starts with a fertilized egg or a bit of living tissue and proceeds through a series of regular stages to the production of a mature individual, as if to an end or goal. So closely knit is this developing system that if it is in any way disrupted it tends to restore itself, as in the healing of wounds, the regeneration of lost parts, and the constant monitorship by which the healthy balance of the body is maintained against threats of injury or disease. Life itself is the manifestation of this organizing activity that dominates an otherwise random mass of matter and makes of it a living system, directed toward a particular culmination. Life, so to speak, imposes organization upon matter.

The seat and center of the control by which this is accomplished is protoplasm, the remarkable physical basis of all life. One might expect that the secret of organized development would lie in the specific chemical character of this material—in hormones, enzymes, or others of the wide array of substances that have been found to affect vital processes. We look to biochemistry for the solution of such a variety of problems in the life sciences that many have tried to find within its field the clue to biological organization. The conclusion seems inescapable, however, that it is not the *character* of the protoplasmic components but the *relations* between them that hold the secret of a living organism. Merely to assemble a group of chemical substances, no matter how specific or carefully chosen they may be, will never bring them to life. "We cannot hope," said E. B. Wilson, "to comprehend the activities of the living cell by an analysis merely of its chemical composition. . . . The cell is an *organic system* and one in which we must recognize some kind of ordered structure or organization." [1] An organism is not simply a mixture of compounds but a living architecture, no part of which can be understood except with reference to the whole.

What has all this to do, you may ask, with the question posed at the beginning of our discussions—with man's dualism, his strange division into body and mind, the material and the apparently immaterial elements of which he is composed? The answer is not far to seek. Since both development and behavior display this same organized directiveness, these two biological processes, one concerned with the body

[1] *The Cell in Development and Heredity* (New York: The Macmillan Company, 3d ed., 1925) , p. 670.

and the other with the mind, seem to have a common basis. If their origin and relations can better be understood, man's dual nature may prove to have a deeper unity beneath it. To explore this relationship requires some further technical discussion. It also demands an excursion into speculation that may seem to many so unrealistic as not only to promise few results of usefulness but to introduce into the sober realms of biological thought a flavor of metaphysics that has no business there. When orthodox conceptions prove unfruitful, however, a little scientific heterodoxy may not be amiss.

The Similarity between Development and Behavior

The thesis I propose to defend is not original, but it has rarely been given the consideration it deserves, nor have its implications been explored as far as is attempted here. If it prove valueless, no harm is done; if sound, it may provide an important unifying concept to bring biology and psychology together much more closely, to the advantage of these sciences and perhaps of philosophy as well. Briefly, it is this: That the insistent tendency among living things for bodily development to reach and maintain, as a norm or goal, an organized living system of a definite kind, and the equally persistent directiveness or goal-seeking that is the essential feature of behavior, and thus finally the basis of all mental activity, are *fundamentally the same thing,* merely two aspects of the basic regulatory character all living stuff displays. Regulation implies something to regulate *to,* a norm or goal. The goal in embryonic life may be regarded as the series of stages that lead to a mature and properly functioning individual; and the goal in psychic life as a purpose or series of purposes, simple and unconscious in primitive instinct, but rising in the mind of man to far higher levels. Mental activity is the most complex form and culmination of that universal regulatory behavior in life which we have been discussing. All ideas, all types of mental life, seem to have been purposes at first. Said William James, "No actions but such as are done for an end . . . are indubitable expressions of mind." [2]

That instinct regulates behavior needs little argument. An organism tends so to adjust itself to its surroundings that normal conditions within it are maintained. When any outside factor menaces its welfare the organism reacts in such a way as to restore these normal conditions. If the temperature becomes too high, it moves to a cooler spot. If danger threatens, it may hide or run. In this way it is able to find a suitable habitat, avoid its enemies, capture food, and in other ways adjust itself to its environment. That its normal activity is usually such as to insure the continuance of the individual's life and the perpetuation of its species results from the action of natural selection. It is not *inherently* favorable, however. Patterns of instinctive behavior, as of development, which are not conducive to survival often appear by mutation or otherwise, but these are such handicaps that in nature they are soon eliminated.

The conclusion that bodily development and instinctive behavior resemble each other in their common purposefulness has impressed a number of biologists and philosophers. "We recognize the fact," says E. S. Russell, "that organic activities, as manifested by organized unities such as cells and organisms, show characteristics, especially their

[2] In all this it is important to define our use of terms. A *goal* I regard as the end toward which development or behavior is directed. The effect of the operation of this goal on the living system is experienced inwardly as a *purpose* if one intends to achieve the goal, or as a *desire* if one is simply attracted toward it.

directiveness, persistency, and adaptability, which are shown also in the instinctive and intelligent behavior of ourselves and other animals. . . . Human directiveness and purposiveness in thought and action are a specialized development of the directiveness and creativeness inherent in life." [3]

Says Karl Heim, describing a living organism, "The theme is that of a self-contained wholeness, over which, like a leading idea, there stands a characteristic form, which builds itself up out of material from its environment, maintains itself by doing battle against all threatening disturbances, and multiplies itself indefinitely if no limits are imposed on its increase. In front of each natural entity there stands 'a picture of what it ought to be,' a form for whose realization it strives with all its powers." [4]

The close relation of instinct to biological organization is often mentioned by Bergson. "Most instincts," he says, "are only the continuance, or rather the consummation, of the work of organization itself. . . . In the metamorphoses of the larva into the nymph and into the perfect insect . . . there is no sharp line of demarcation between the instinct of the animal and the organizing work of living matter. We may say, as we will, either that instinct organizes the instruments it is about to use, or that the process of organization is continued in the instinct that has to use the organ." [5]

Ralph Lillie has discussed the matter in a notable book. "The general conclusion to which we are led by these considerations," he says, "is that in living organisms physical integration and psychical integration represent two aspects,

<hr />

[3] *The Directiveness of Organic Activities* (Cambridge: Cambridge University Press, 1945), p. 179.
[4] *The Transformation of the Scientific World View* (New York: Harper and Brothers, 1954), p. 214.
[5] Henri Bergson, *Creative Evolution*, translated by A. Mitchell (New York: Modern Library, 1911), p. 139.

corresponding to two mutually complementary sets of factors, of one and the same biological process." [6]

Some psychologists take essentially this position and are inclined to interpret all behavior as homeostatic, as tending to maintain or restore the individual in a favorable situation or condition. One recent text goes so far as to define psychology as "the study of those homeostatic processes which involve the whole organism." [7]

The idea that goal-seeking in both development and behavior has a common basis in the regulatory character of all living stuff therefore has enough to commend it so that it deserves a sympathetic hearing. If the concept is a sound one a study of the biological basis of regulation in the relatively simple examples of it to be met in growth and development may help us understand the more complex ones presented by behavior.

Body, Mind, and Purpose

The regulatory mechanism by which a plant or animal in its development moves toward a precise end is obviously a problem open to scientific investigation, and it has been widely studied. As to just what this mechanism is, however, there is great uncertainty, and the matter need not concern us at the moment. *Something* there is in the living stuff of the organism to which growth conforms—something, so to speak, that represents the developmental history of the whole individual.

The simplest example of this is a fertilized egg cell. It has a very specific constitution of thousands of hereditary units

[6] Ralph S. Lillie, *General Biology and Philosophy of Organism* (Chicago: University of Chicago Press, 1945), p. 46.
[7] Ross Stagner and T. F. Karwoski, *Psychology* (New York: McGraw-Hill Company, 1952), p. 19.

or genes. The triumph of the science of genetics in the past half-century has been to prove that these units occur as actual physical entities in the threadlike chromosomes of the nucleus, that each occupies a very precise location in a particular chromosome, and that each influences a specific developmental process. This great complex of genes, each coordinated so precisely in its activity with all the rest in embryonic development that they do not block or impede one another, leads to the production of an adult individual of a very definite character. How this is accomplished remains unknown save for a few hints here and there, and poses the chief problem before genetics today. Some sort of organization among these genes there must be, something that exactly foreshadows the step-by-step developmental process that will form the individual produced from this egg. Just as the form and character of this mature individual are thus immanent, though yet unrealized, in the egg from which it grows, so, I suggest, a purpose yet to be realized may be immanent in the cells of the brain. Conformity to such a purpose, an act of biological regulation, is the basis of behavior. A *conscious* purpose is the inner experience of this protoplasmic goal-seeking.

What comes from the egg is a structure, and from the purpose an act. These at first sight seem very different, but we should remember that both are results of the activity of living protoplasm. No sharp line can well be drawn between the familiar processes of bodily development and the physiological activities that accompany them, such as breathing and the circulation of the blood. These, in turn, are in a sense the beginnings of behavior and are hard to separate from rudimentary instincts. At the end of its embryonic growth within the egg, as Bergson remarks, a young chick breaks the shell by a peck of its beak. This surely is an instinctive act, the beginning of behavior, but it is simply the culmination of the processes of development and physiological activity. One might carry the idea still further and say that such a formative activity as the building of a bird's nest is simply a continuation, as instinct, of the constructive processes of development. There seems no reason to separate the admittedly unknown regulatory activities that go on in the cells of the brain, which underlie behavior, from the equally unknown ones responsible for orderly, goal-directed bodily development and function.

The goal of the organism, implanted first in the genetic constitution of the egg, unfolds itself in structure and activity as development progresses. In every cell of the body, so it seems, are to be found the same genes, derived from those first present in the egg. These cells gradually become different as growth proceeds, until the great diversity of structure present in tissues and organs of the mature individual is reached. This goal is not a static one, gained once for all, for genetic control does not cease when growth is ended but extends to the behavior of the mature organism. At all levels the organism is held to a straight course by constant regulation, which brings it back whenever it deviates from the norm. The pattern of development and activity that works itself out in this way is not the result of a mere collection of independent genes, like beads on a string or marbles in a bag or separate chemical substances, but of a precisely integrated and continuing *relationship* between them. It has well been said that the organism is not an aggregate but an integrate. The nature of this relationship is the basic and still unsolved problem of biology.

In each of the various examples of self-regulation that are described in earlier pages of this book there is an implanted pattern of development which is the biological goal. How this is set up and how it is attained; what the means are by which genes and their products are bound into a system that so permeates the whole and is so resilient that a loss or change in any part calls forth a regulatory alteration in growth—these are problems of tremendous difficulty. My thesis is that they are basically the *same* problems as those of psychological regulation. They can better be attacked experimentally, perhaps, at the level of embryology and physiology than at the level of psychology, but there is no reason to think that the physical basis of embryonic self-regulation is any simpler than, or perhaps in essence any different from, the regulation of behavior that occurs in the nervous system.

This emphasis on the regulatory character of mind may help make clear one of its fundamental functions. In all living things there are mechanisms that receive and react to stimulation. The more complex animals possess sense organs, which are sensitive to stimuli and transmit them to a central clearing-house, the brain. Another portion of the nervous system controls the reaction to this stimulus, muscular or otherwise. The stimulus-response relationship is fundamental in psychology and goes back in origin to the irritability or reactivity of all living stuff. To regard human behavior, or animal behavior in general, as nothing more than a series of responses to stimuli, however, is to cherish far too simple a view of it. Reflex action is important, but it is by no means everything. A particular response does not inevitably and invariably follow a particular stimulus in the way that the discharge of a bullet follows the stimulus of a trigger-pull or as a bell rings in an alarm clock when the hand reaches a critical position. Between stimulus and response in an organism, something very important occurs, an act of *regulation*. What the response will be depends on the norm or purpose set up in the living system, for the response will tend to maintain or restore that norm. How an animal reacts—even the tiniest and simplest of animals—depends on its inner state. A hungry one will respond to a food stimulus very differently from one that is fully fed, for a particular physiological goal has been attained in one but not in the other. The relation of stimulus to response, if written S–R, lacks an important element—the organism, O. It should be set down as S–O–R, for the organized living system that comes between the two is vitally important. To maintain its norms is the ultimate function of the nervous system.

The brain is a mass of extraordinarily sensitive and reactive living cells in which, so to speak, the self-regulatory capacity is concentrated and intensified. Just where and how this is done is still a mystery, though the inner reticular system of the cortex may in some way be concerned in it. The relation between brain and "mind" is as far as ever from being understood, but to the layman it is tempting to think that what is here involved is the ancient regulatory character of protoplasm that underlies all life. A nervous system is far better developed in animals than in plants (indeed, plants can hardly be said to have one), since animals, which cannot make their own food and must therefore move actively about in search of it, are required to make behavioral regulations frequently and often rapidly. The nervous system is the mechanism by which this is accomplished, and what we call conscious mind is our experience of this intense regulatory activity. We have brains—and minds—because our hungry ancestors had to evolve them to keep from starving.

The higher functions of the mind, though far removed from the simple regulations of protoplasm, may nevertheless also be interpreted, I think, in terms of biological purposiveness. The simplest of ideas are purposes. For primitive man, thought led at once to bodily action. Only later did he find it possible to substitute mental acts for physical ones, imagining deeds without actually performing them. Still later, through the further development of memory and imagination, and by the manipulation of spoken and written symbols, grew the power of abstract thought. What thought is and how it has developed are vast problems, quite beyond the competence of the present study. That cerebral activity at these topmost levels grew out of more primitive mental processes is a conclusion that, as good evolutionists, we are bound to accept; and these simpler processes, in turn, as we have seen, can be related to the fundamental regulatory purposiveness of life. Mind is the highest of biological phenomena, but it is a biological process, nevertheless.

The Creativeness of Life

In addition to the regulatory character that both display, there is a further similarity between the development and the behavior of living things. Both produce novelties in nature. Both are *creative*.

An organism draws in random material from its environment and builds this into a living system which it maintains against the disruptive tendencies of the lifeless world. Life is inherently synthetic, and synthesis is an organizing process. It puts substances together to make the almost infinite number of organic compounds found in the bodies of animals and plants. During the course of evolution this synthetic process has steadily produced *new* compounds, substances never known before on earth. More than this, new species—new organized systems—have also been developed. The fascination for us of the great evolutionary drama is to watch the continuous procession of them which comes upon the scene. These developments may be related, as many believe, to the almost limitless possibilities for new atomic combinations among compounds of carbon; but whatever the cause, we must admit that life in its material products is persistently creative. Such creativeness is not evident in the inorganic world. So far as the cosmogonists can tell us, the various chemical elements that form the universe were all produced at its creation or shortly thereafter. Some transmutations and combinations among them there certainly have been, but nothing like the fantastic outburst of new substances and systems that life has made. Constancy and conservatism are qualities of the lifeless, not the living.

In a similar fashion, psychical activity is creative. Even homeostasis, so evident in physiological processes, is not to be thought of as merely the maintenance of a static condition, for its norms change as development progresses. It is in behavior, however, that the constant change in goals and the origin of new ones are most conspicuous. As Lillie puts it, "Psychical existence is in present time and carries with it a quality of novelty; the past is left behind, and there is an advance into the future. . . . The psychical is the source of initiative when action takes on a novel, unforeseen, or creative form, as in purposive activity or (in a broader sense) in natural creative action in general." [8] Whitehead has expressed this idea in a famous line: "The psychical is a part of the creative advance into novelty."

From the synthesis of a new substance by an organism, or the origin of a new species, to supreme creations in the imagination of an artist or a poet, we are dealing with the same restless, changeful, trail-blazing quality of life that

[8] Ralph S. Lillie, loc. cit., p. 161.

is found at all its levels. This creativeness, common to both the physical and the behavioral aspects of living stuff, is further evidence, it seems to me, that the highest expressions of both—the body and the mind of man—grow from a fundamental unity.

Objections to the Hypothesis

But despite its plausibility, this concept that mind is not a separate and distinctive thing but is an aspect of biological organization and goal-seeking will not readily be accepted by many. A conscious purpose in the mind and an embryonic process in a developing tadpole appear at first to be so far apart that to regard them as fundamentally the same sort of thing may seem indeed preposterous. Certainly no solution to man's dualism as simple and pat as this will meet wide agreement or fail to evoke serious argument. At least three objections to it come at once to mind. Reasonable answers are at hand for them, I believe, but to present these will require a more detailed discussion of the basic idea itself.

In the first place the suggestion, although founded on biological evidence, goes counter to an important tenet of the life sciences. Biology has only recently won the right to be considered a true science in the modern sense, based on unvarying lawfulness, as physics is, and free at last from childish ideas that plants and animals have human qualities. Scientists have fought so hard to keep the insidious idea of purpose *out* of biology that they will not readily assent to a concept that puts this fighting word back at the very heart of the life sciences. Slipshod teaching has so often falsely appealed to "purpose" that the very word has become anathema to many. One reads in some texts, for example, that roots are "for the purpose" of absorbing water and nutrients from the soil or that the "purpose" of a fawn's dappled coat is to make him inconspicuous in the forest. A teacher often slips into terminology like this for ease of explanation, rather than discussing the more difficult ideas of natural selection or physiological mechanisms. The student thus gets the wrong conception that living things are *trying to adapt themselves* to their surroundings and succeed through some mysterious power to do what is best for themselves.

But "purpose" of this sort is in no way implied in the suggestion that is here presented, which provides a scientific basis for purpose. It requires an acceptance of no mysterious power to do whatever is advantageous. The problems of developmental regulation, of the factors that control embryology in the broad sense, of what the biologist calls *morphogenesis,* are certainly in the domain of science. Innumerable studies have been made in an attempt to find what determines the form and structure of a growing animal or plant. The question is always approached, however, from the orthodox viewpoint of scientific determinism— that one event follows another in a regular and constant fashion. To introduce into this system what seems to be a "final" cause, something existing in the mind that leaps, as it were, across the gap between cause and effect, may seem to break up the necessary continuity between these events, and to interject into the process an element that violates the orderliness of nature, which is the necessary foundation of science.

The idea I have been trying to present, however, need not violate this orderliness at all. The norm or goal or ideal set up in protoplasm, to which development conforms, may turn out to be as mechanical as the "goal" of a thermostat set for seventy degrees. If one wishes to reduce this idea to absurdity he may suggest that a stretched bow has a "purpose" to shoot an arrow, or even that a stone has a "purpose" to roll downhill! It may be that purpose can be explained at last in terms of present physical concepts, as have so many other biological problems. This may never happen. Living systems seem to be unique in nature and may well require unique ideas to account for them. Only in life is there evidence of something integrating and creative in the universe. Whatever life's physical basis may be, of one thing we can be sure: there *is* inherent in the living system a self-regulating quality that keeps it directed toward a definite norm or course, and the growth and activity of the organism takes place in conformity to it. How this will finally come to be interpreted in adequate scientific and philosophical terms is the basic problem.

In addition to this general scientific objection to purpose, such a concept is also contrary to the accepted ideas of the particular science of psychology. It suggests that the behavior of an organism results from its being drawn toward something, desiring something, whereas orthodox psychology, grounded in physiology and the physical sciences, is obliged to think of behavior as the result of a push or drive. Such drives of many sorts are recognized and are being widely studied—hunger, sex, fear, ambition, and many more. They are thought of as resulting from a chain of physical causes fundamentally like those that drive a machine. This idea makes physiological sense, for it is the sort of causation we are accustomed to assume in chemical and physical reactions. To the layman, however, it presents a serious difficulty, for it does not explain the precise *directiveness* of behavior. Drive will provide an organism's motive power, as it does for a car, but without something to steer it the car will have no goal, and its direction will be aimless. An automatic and self-guiding machine, like an airplane flying blind on instruments, does possess such directiveness, but this, you will observe, comes not from the drive of the propellers but from an inner regulating mechanism. This is set for a particular course. As soon as the plane gets off this course the mechanism operates at once to pull it back on again. This is a crude picture, I think, of how a specific purpose, set up in the brain or in any other protoplasmic system, guides behavior. To call this a "drive" seems a misnomer. The concept here proposed is closer to reality. It can be interpreted in as mechanistic terms as one pleases, but the point of view is very different from that of the idea of "drive." In an organism the mechanism is extremely delicate and in the human brain reaches fantastic complexity, but it is presumably much the same everywhere. When a living thing gets off its course toward a purposed goal a "tension"—this is the psychologist's word and an expressive one—is set up, which tends to put it right again.

Through the concept of purpose here proposed it is also possible to take account of other psychological facts that fit less well into accepted theory. Only rarely do we have an inner sense of being pushed or driven. On the contrary, we feel as if there were something toward which we were being drawn, something we *want*. Introspection, to be sure, is somewhat outmoded in these days as a valid avenue to truth in psychology, but we should not forget that a man is inside his most important biological specimen, himself, and that from this strategic position he is able to learn many things that no amount of observation of other specimens ever could reveal. One of the most important facts about man is that he is a wanting, desiring, longing, aspiring animal. Indeed, this is the essence of him and the source of his power. It cannot be dismissed as insignificant. Wants and desires can be interpreted in terms of drive, to be sure, but they can more readily be accounted for, it seems to me, as the inner experience of the drawing power of a goal set up within. Desire is the first step toward purpose. Wanting food slips almost automatically into a purpose to obtain it. Sometimes, however, this goes no further, since many purposes are either conflicting or unattainable. But what we want, the orientation of our minds *toward* something, is the effect on us of an inner goal, whether we can reach it or not.

The difference between the contrasting concepts of "drive" and "goal," of being pushed or being drawn, seems to me much more than a quibble. It involves two unlike views of the basis of all organic activity. We are so mechanically minded that the concept of drive seems more natural to us. Actually, the idea of being drawn provides a more accurate picture of our motives *as we experience them*. The hunger drive is simply a strong desire for food, which makes us seek it actively. We do not seem to be pushed toward food, compelled to seek it, but try eagerly to reach it by our own efforts. The drive for success or power means that we want these things very much. We recognize no compulsion to do so. The results, of course, are much the same in either case, but the interpretation that we choose has important consequences for our philosophy. The essential question is whether our behavior is due to something outside us, a stimulus that sets off a drive reaction in our protoplasmic mechanism, or to something that has its origin inside, something spontaneous and at least in part independent of external control. The psychologist will doubtless be loath to surrender his concept of drive, but it is important to remind him, I think, that a motive may be looked at from the front, so to speak, as well as from the rear. The concepts of "drive" and "draw" are both in harmony with physiological orthodoxy if we regard goal-seeking as mechanical regulation; but the latter has the advantage that it provides an interpretation of behavior that explains certain facts, notably the data from our inner feelings, that the former must ignore.[9]

By defining the concept of purpose in these terms, therefore, one can make it biologically respectable again and relieve it from the stigma of "final" causation and mysticism. As Herbert J. Muller has well said, "Purpose is not imported into nature, and need not be puzzled over as a strange or divine something else that gets inside and makes life go; it is no more an added force than mind is something in addition to brain. It is simply implicit in the fact of organization, and it is to be studied rather than admired or 'explained.' " [10] One must only be careful not to ascribe naïve purposefulness, conscious or unconscious, to plants or animals, as Lamarck did, or to assume that living things will always do what is best for them because of some inner power. The beautiful adaptations of organisms to their environment, which have excited so much curiosity and wonder among naturalists, can be accounted for by the orderly processes of natural selection without appealing to anything further.

There is always the possibility that "final" causes actually *may* be operative in nature and that a purpose in the mind may have a direct effect on physical events. For such a philosophy our concept of organic purposiveness would provide a biological foundation. Teleology still has its defenders, and among men of science there are some who are

[9] The concept of drive in motivation is further discussed in Chapter IV.
[10] *Science and Criticism* (New Haven: Yale University Press, 1943), p. 109.

unable to account for all the facts of nature without invoking it to some degree. Perhaps the conflict between this concept and the mechanical determinism of science may never be resolved. L. J. Henderson ends his detailed discussion of the subject on a somewhat pessimistic note. "Nothing more remains," he says, "but to admit that the riddle surpasses us and to conclude that the contrast of mechanism with teleology is the very foundation of the order of nature, which must ever be regarded from two complementary points of view." [11] D'Arcy Thompson in his biological classic, *On Growth and Form,* comes to much the same conclusion: "Still, all the while, like warp and woof, mechanism and teleology are interwoven together . . . their union is rooted in the very nature of totality." [12] But the problem now has slipped far into metaphysics and need not here concern us further.

A second and perhaps more serious objection to our hypothesis is that purpose, in the commonly accepted meaning of the word, is *conscious* purpose, a deliberate intention in the mind. There is no conscious mind, you may assert, in the lower animals, and certainly none in plants. Consciousness is something that has developed with the increasing complexity of the brain and is associated with that fantastically intricate mechanism the cerebral cortex, and its billions of nerve cells. Purposiveness of this sort may have a superficial resemblance to embryonic regulation, but it is only superficial. To regard these processes as fundamentally the same is to stretch analogy until it breaks.

But consciousness is difficult to define. It forms a problem by itself and need not necessarily be concerned, I think, in

[11] *The Order of Nature* (Cambridge, Mass.: Harvard University Press, 1917), p. 209.
[12] Sir D'Arcy W. Thompson, *On Growth and Form* (Cambridge: Cambridge University Press, 2nd ed., 1942), p. 7.

the fact of biological purposiveness. Consciousness is a state of mental awareness, not merely physical sensitivity. Although man is the being who seems pre-eminently to possess consciousness, the beginnings of it are clearly present in the higher vertebrates, as are the beginnings of mind— or our Societies for the Prevention of Cruelty to Animals are much deceived! But what about animals still lower? Here the ancient interrogation still confronts us. Just where, in the long evolutionary progression from protozoan to primate, did consciousness, and mind, first come to being? If they are functions of the brain, we must admit that brains of a sort are found far down among the simpler animals. These in turn must have evolved from something simpler still. The very lowest animals and the whole plant kingdom lack brains or even organized nervous systems, but still are able to carry on, though in a primitive and sluggish fashion, most of the activities that in higher forms are under the control of nervous tissue. We need not assume, says Bergson, that consciousness "involves as a necessary condition the presence of a nervous system; the latter has only canalized in definite directions, and brought up to a higher degree of intensity, a rudimentary and vague activity, diffused through the mass of the organized substance." [13]

As good evolutionists we must believe, I think, that brain and mind and consciousness in man came from far more primitive beginnings, and that the germ of each is in all living stuff. In practice, of course, we may distinguish vivid "focal" consciousness from the deep layers of the "unconscious" below it, as in practice we may distinguish what we call man's mind from its prototype in the animals; but the most profound philosophical question the theory of evolution posed was just *where* such attributes as these, which

[13] Henri Bergson, loc. cit., p. 110.

we used to think of as limited to man, actually first came to being.

Purpose is rooted much more deeply in protoplasm than consciousness is. Indeed, no inconsiderable advantage of the conception here proposed is that it moves consciousness out of the center of the picture. Many philosophers are so concerned with the phenomena of that part of mental life which involves conscious activity—perception, connation, thought, and the rest—that their problems become at once involved. It is at the conscious level, of course, that man's life as a rational being emerges from that of the brute creation, with all the changes that must follow this; but the line between the conscious and the unconscious is blurred and may often change. Acts that at first are conscious ones may through habitual performance lose this quality. Others, like breathing, deeply rooted in the nervous system, hardly rise to consciousness at all, and purely physiological activities never do. Modern psychology stresses the great importance of what goes on in our unconscious minds. All aspects of mental life, one can maintain, are subject to the basic, purposive self-regulation of life in general, but an *awareness* of this—consciousness—is limited to the upper levels of the process. Just how consciousness began we cannot be sure, but it seems reasonable to attribute its appearance to the increasing crises of choice that arose between the vastly expanding number of goals that were offered as organisms ascended in complexity.

A third objection is also serious. Granted that in embryology there is something that might be called a goal or purpose, or even an "idea," this is such a simple, single-track sort of mental process that it cannot be thought of as a basis for the constantly changing stream of mental life in man, enriched as this is with memory, imagination, association, and abstract thought. The difference between these two, you may say, is so very great that it becomes no longer one of quantity but of quality. If a bean plant has a "mind" it is surely a very different sort of thing from man's.

Here it is necessary to see clearly the relation between this universal goal-seeking quality of organisms, inherent in their living stuff, and the influence environment exerts on the nature of the goals that are being sought. In every kind of plant and animal an inborn genetic constitution does not lead to a single goal but often reaches different goals under different conditions. Thus a water-buttercup growing on a muddy bank with only its roots in water forms leaves much like those of other species of buttercup, but when it grows submerged its leaves are finely divided into long, narrow segments. Each type is "normal"; each is the plant's goal under a particular environment; but the expression of its genetic constitution differs radically, depending on conditions. Similarly, some plants, like cosmos, flower early and profusely if the days are relatively long, but form nothing but vigorous leafy shoots in seasons with shorter days. The young embryo of a sea urchin has a very different shape from the usual one if it is grown in water where lithium is present in excess; but both types are normal, both are embryonic goals. The small fruit fly *Drosophila*, which has been so important in the history of genetics, shows even more complex relationships between environment and hereditary expression, since the development of many characteristics of body and wing is affected by the temperature at which the early stages are reared. The genetic constitution of an organism has not just one developmental goal but a whole repertoire of them. All living things regulate their growth toward goals, but what goals actually are achieved depends in part on inborn qualities and in part on the environment. Goals change with conditions, as they do at higher levels of life.

Self-regulation in instinctive behavior shows much greater diversity, for every change in the environment calls for a responsive adjustment to maintain normal life, and these adjustments must obviously be far more rapid than are the sluggish responses made in growth and development. For such an animal as a clam, almost stationary in its buried chamber, the environment changes slowly. To maintain it in a normal state not many regulatory responses are necessary. Its "desires" are few, and its "mental" life simple in the extreme. A bee, on the other hand, which moves actively from flower to flower, necessarily must deal with a rapidly changing environment. Its basic goal—that of a normal and successful existence—is broken up into a series of subordinate ones. It seeks out particular kinds of flowers, extracts nectar or pollen from them, finds its way back to the hive, communicates in various ways with its fellows, and thus leads a relatively complex life. Every step is one of purposive activity, directed to the attainment of one goal or another—often fleeting, but always related to the fundamental goal.

Students of animal psychology have found that in many cases there is a series of fixed patterns or norms of response that are "released" by particular environmental factors, so that instinctive behavior in such cases consists of attempts to realize one norm or another in the animal's repertoire. The "mental" life of an active animal, especially one of the vertebrates, albeit still at an instinctive level, shows a variety which begins to approach that of man. Here again there is no sharp line anywhere in the hierarchy of norms and purposes. Between the turning of a flower toward the light and the pattern of behavior of a bee there is a continuous series of intermediates, and the difference between a bee and a man, in the fundamental mechanics of their activities, seems to be one of degree rather than of kind. Man, to be sure, by the prodigious complexity of his brain and his high development of memory, imagination, and reasoning power, is set apart as a unique species in the world of living things; but the great variety and changefulness of his mental life seem to have arisen through a series of steps from much simpler prototypes. Regulation in all cases is not to a static goal but to an ever-changing series of them. Man's stream of changing mental life can be interpreted, I think, as simply the highest manifestation of the same regulatory, purposive activity that all life displays.

So runs the argument for a unifying concept of body and mind. If valid, it will help break down the traditional idea that these two parts of man are quite unlike and that he necessarily must be a dual creature, divided against himself. Much further evidence to the same conclusion might be presented from both biology and psychology. It is a defensible idea, I think, and worthy of respectful consideration, that what we call the mind is but the highest and most complex expression of that self-regulating, goal-seeking quality manifest in the activities of all living things. The mental and the developmental are simply two aspects of the same basic, vital process. Life and mind essentially are one. Mind is not something limited to the human brain, or to any brain, but its primitive beginnings are to be found in the activity of every living cell. Only with the evolution of the nervous system in animals, and the complex patterns of behavior that result, does the regulation of *activity* begin to seem distinct from the regulation of *growth*—does the mind, in short, begin to seem distinct from the body.

A great advantage of the idea here presented is that it enables us at least to bring the ancient discussion about mind and body down out of the nebulous stratosphere of conjecture into the laboratory. The secret of self-regulation in growth and development is a biological problem on which a vast amount of scientific work has been carried on and which is a particularly active field of biology today. Whatever is discovered here—and the problem of self-regulation is an obdurate one that is very far from being solved—will be of value for an understanding of behavior, and thus ultimately of mind itself.

One should remember too that this helpful service of biology to psychology need not be one-sided but may work in the other direction as well. If mind is an expression of biological self-regulation, whatever can be learned about mind *as such* should help interpret life at much lower levels. The most complex expression of a process may be studied as profitably as the simplest one, for it often shows possibilities that would otherwise remain quite unsuspected. All the activities we have been discussing are biological, and biology in its deepest sense stretches from cell to psyche.

CHAPTER IV

Of Men and Motives

Abstract

The chief practical significance of the hypothesis here presented is in its interpretation of human motives. The great importance of the strength and direction of motives is emphasized and illustrated. Differences in motive are often more effective in determining achievement than differences in natural gifts.

Most psychologists interpret motives as drives, rooted in physiological processes. These are of many sorts and at many levels. If goal-seeking is a general quality of all life, however, motives are to be regarded as based on wants or desires, the results of being *drawn* toward something rather than of being *driven*. This concept provides directiveness, which a drive lacks. It is also in agreement with man's inner convictions.

To achieve moral conduct, necessary for a successful social order, dependence has usually been placed on law and education. These are important, but each has weaknesses for this purpose. What chiefly determines a man's conduct is what he *wants* to do. The necessity of elevating his desires must therefore be recognized. To make people want to do what they ought to do is a very important but often neglected problem. To accomplish this, attention to a proposed goal must first be gained. This may awaken interest in it. Through

75

the contagion of ideas from books and other sources, interest leads to the growth of new desires. The role of contagious personalities in teachers and moral leaders is also of great importance.

A recognition of the essential part played by goals in human behavior therefore not only makes possible a clearer understanding of man's nature but may lead to more effective means of determining his motives and thus of guiding his conduct.

The concept that both bodily development and behavior —the bases of body and of mind—are expressions, though in two different ways, of that self-regulation and goal-seeking evident in all activities of living stuff is thus no idle speculation. In its support there can be marshaled a body of evidence well worthy of attention and respect. To accept it is to cast aside the ancient dualistic conception of man's nature, which would have us think of him as two distinct and quite dissimilar beings. By it his unity can be restored. Just what this self-regulating quality of living things may be in terms of matter and of energy is a problem for biology and can properly be attacked as such; but it is equally a problem for psychology if developmental processes have led to mental ones. Such a unifying idea provides a foundation on which the superstructure of both these sciences can be erected. The primary concern of each is protoplasmic purposiveness.

As a theory, this is attractive, since it serves to bring into a single pattern many diverse and apparently unrelated facts. Its consequences for philosophy are far from negligible. But the practical aspect of the idea that mind and body have a common origin also commends it to our attention, for it suggests that if goal-seeking is a fundamental quality of living stuff a study of it may disclose the source of those forces that control the direction and intensity of human motives. Here is the central problem of behavior, the decisive factor in all conduct. The essence of our thesis is that man is not only a rational being but fundamentally a seeking, desiring, aspiring one. From this comes the force that moves and guides him. *What* he seeks is widely various. It depends in part on his inborn predispositions but also, in no small measure, on the environment and training to which he is exposed. This possibility that his goals may be elevated and the power of his aspiring nature harnessed to good ends is what gives hope of making our social order a far better one than it now is.

Man does have motive power that is his own. He is not simply at the mercy of external agencies, strong and compelling as these obviously are. Something inside him helps direct his course. On the river of circumstance he still is borne along; but he moves there not inertly, like a log, but as a boat moves that contains within it power enough to give it steerage way at least, and sometimes even to carry it upstream against the current.

Motives are subtle qualities and often hard to analyze. Their origin, I think, is in goals and purposes, consciously felt or operating in the deeper regions of the unconscious mind. Men differ most profoundly in what they want and in the strength with which they want it. The fascination of biography is not primarily in the story of a career or in the way a man is tossed about by fate and circumstance. What interests us most is the immanence in him of some goal eagerly sought, and the persistence with which he overcomes the obstacles to its attainment. This is the axis around which the fabric of his life is always built. What we most wish to know about him is not what he did but what he *wanted* to do, the inner urgencies at work within him.

The Power of Motives

Examples of the power of motivation are everywhere familiar in history and in our experience. Consider Jonathan Edwards. From his early college days he wrestled with great ideas. There slowly grew within him, until it dominated his whole life, a high ambition—to build a logical system of theology that should place Man and the Church and Christ and God in their proper relations to one another and serve to bring all men to an understanding of the Truth. Despite the demands of a large parish and a growing family, in the cold of parsonage studies and the heat of long and earnest disputations, he moved steadily toward this goal. Edwards was intimately concerned with the Great Awakening, but while its echoes still reverberated through the New England hills a violent quarrel in the Northampton church led to his dismissal from its pulpit, and the town forbade his preaching within its boundaries again. The most brilliant philosopher and theologian of his time was thus forced to migrate to the frontier hamlet of Stockbridge in the hills of western Massachusetts, there to minister to its little church and serve as missionary to the Housatonic Indians. Even through these calamities, however, he did not falter in his single-minded purpose. The intrigues of white men and the threats of red ones could not divert him from it. Out of the seclusion of those wilderness years came *The Freedom of the Will,* his attempt to discover how the human spirit can be free in a world whose fate is fixed and absolute—a goal to which philoso-

phers still address themselves. Other great books followed
this. Such an ambition was not one to appeal to many, then
or now—simply a row of books and a tidy clearing in the
wilderness of ignorance and error, where the Word could
be sown and Truth come finally to harvest. Whence, we may
ask, came his indomitable purpose? What was the source of
the motive power that led him on?

Or look at young Charles Darwin. In his early years he
was uncertain where his life should lead. School he dis-
liked, but he enjoyed the out-of-doors and grouse shooting,
as an English country gentleman should. At last he went
to Edinburgh to study medicine, but found that, too, intol-
erable. Then his wealthy father stepped in and sent him
to Cambridge to prepare himself to be a clergyman of the
Church of England. His record in the university was undis-
tinguished, but outside his formal class work he became
interested in natural history, collected beetles actively, and
learned a little botany and geology as well. After taking his
degree in 1831, he would have entered Holy Orders in due
course, had there not come an opportunity to serve as naturalist on the *Beagle,* a British man-of-war about to under-
take a long voyage to the southern hemisphere. Overcoming
his father's opposition, he sailed away and spent five years
collecting plants and animals and their fossils in distant
regions of the earth.

This experience gave him a new and vital interest. He
began to see the serious difficulties in accounting for the
character and distribution of living things by a literal interpretation of the creation narrative in the first chapter
of Genesis, and on a memorable day, while he was collecting in the Galápagos Islands, it occurred to him that these
difficulties would vanish if plants and animals had slowly
evolved through the ages instead of springing into being

all at once. So tremendous was this idea that it dominated his life from that time forward. He "opened a notebook" on the subject and gathered facts about it from every possible source. He returned to England, and on another never-to-be-forgotten day—through reading an essay by Malthus—he found the clue to the means of evolutionary change and conceived his famous theory of natural selection.

Darwin was a quiet man, but there grew within him a passion for this great idea and an eagerness to explore it completely. For the rest of his life, in a quiet country home in Kent, he gathered facts and read and wrote and pondered about it. Out of his long ponderings came *The Origin of Species* and many other fruits of his long labors. Through continued ill health that would have overwhelmed a man without his high incentive, Darwin pursued his goal with unflagging determination. This one great purpose—to understand the origin of the infinitely varied differences that distinguish the vast host of living things on earth—transformed an aimless and uncertain young man, without notable gifts or qualities and in danger through his wealth of growing up to be nothing but a "shooting fellow," and made of him a force that shook down ancient orthodoxies and changed the thinking of mankind. All this grew not from outward circumstance—one would never have picked young Darwin as the great man of his century—but from the flood of motive power loosed within him through his capture by this tremendous purpose.

Biography is full of similar examples. Whence come such overmastering purposes as these? The men and women who are stirred by them make vivid to us the tremendous motive power that lies in a great desire. If once it lays hold of a man it can lead him on to heights impossible for those who never know the agony and joy of a mighty longing. When a man connects the terminals of his being to the circuit of some great purpose he is flooded with power to follow and accomplish it. How much this depends on inborn qualities and how much on a propitious environment is one of the great problems of psychology. Let us remember, too, that it is not the worth of a motive that gives it power. Ignoble purposes may generate power as well as lofty ones. The unscrupulous ambition of such a man as Hitler can give him the strength to topple down a world. In these men the force of a great desire that might have carried them to high achievement is debased and turned aside into a destructive course. Great men of every sort impress us not so much by their innate ability as by their dedication to a supreme ambition, be it good or ill. This is the stuff of character. Human history has been molded by the aspirations of that minority of individuals who had the capacity to *want* something very much.

Few there are who can nourish the tremendous motive power that makes great heroes and great villains. In all men, however, there develop patterns of motivation around which their lives crystallize. Domination by a desire may come suddenly, as does religious conversion, but such cases are not common. More frequently the power of purpose grows slowly in a man. Often he may have no central goal, no continuing aspiration, but moves this way and that as the changing winds of purpose blow, drifting along the channel of habit to the doldrums of routine existence. No differences among men are so effective and so difficult to understand as these in spiritual horsepower. Here is involved no balance sheet of calories that records the intake and outgo of our bodily energies—that is simply a problem in physiology—but those deeper spiritual forces welling up within us that determine the strength of our likes and dislikes, our purposes and our determinations. Their sources are hidden, but their effects are beyond all calculation. All of us have known men and women of very modest natural gifts and with intelligence quotients no more than respectable, whose ambition and enthusiastic purposefulness were so strong as to carry their possessors on to high achievement. Many too are those endowed with great inborn abilities who, through lack of determination and desire, never bring them to full fruition. This inner motive power the psychologist finds it very hard to measure. Abilities and aptitudes —the qualities of the human machine—he can evaluate, but the inner dynamic still eludes him.

Individuals differ not only in the strength but in the direction of their desires. The richness and diversity of our society are an expression of the great variety of motives among the people who compose it. One may be dedicated to a career in medicine. Another would be unhappy outside the office of an architect. A third is a born salesman. If necessity and not inclination determines a man's career his natural desires express themselves in his avocations, his hobbies and the ways in which he spends his leisure. These are almost infinitely various, and in them no two men are ever quite alike. What makes freedom precious is the opportunity it gives for the full flowering of the numberless interests and desires of men.

The intensity and the direction of his purposes are the most significant things about a person. Externally men are so much alike that a taxonomist has no difficulty in placing them all within a single species, *Homo sapiens;* but how astonishingly various they are inside, in their likes and dislikes, their attitudes and interests, their emotions, sympathies, and aspirations! The powerful forces of society tend to make men uniform, to standardize them as we do bolts and tires and cartridges. But the inner man bursts through all these restraints and blossoms in an endless variety of thoughts and deeds. Why is he drawn toward some things and repelled by others? What powers him? What steers him? In short, what is the basis for his *motives?* With all our boasted understanding and our growing knowledge, biological and psychological, about man, this deepest question is still as far from final answer now as it was when Socrates asked it so persistently on the streets of Athens centuries ago.

Psychology and Motives

The psychology of today is ready with at least a tentative answer. Having satisfactorily disposed of the old ideas about the "mind" and the "will," it has now begun a new exploration of man's actions and a new interpretation of his motives. The modern science of behavior is rooted in physiology and orthodox mechanistic theory. It assumes that man's body, like that of every other living thing, is a physico-chemical machine, no different in essence from any lifeless mechanism. What relation body has to mind is still a complex and confusing problem, to be sure, but psychology assumes that the material body is the essential member of the pair, and that in some way mind depends upon it. If the events of bodily physiology are rigidly determined, as all other physical and chemical events now seem to be, and if mental events depend upon them, then surely all motives are at bottom physiological too—aspects of the activity of the living organism, just as are respiration, digestion, and other processes of metabolism.

These assumptions about mind and motivation are natural

ones for psychology to make today and have justified themselves by leading to important discoveries in this field. The relationship, for example, between specific regions of the brain and various mental faculties has repeatedly been shown. Alcohol and drugs of many sorts profoundly change men's mental attitudes and alter the direction and intensity of their desires. The glands of internal secretion are equally effective. Adrenalin, poured into the bloodstream in moments of anger, arouses an individual's belligerent potential. Prolactin, secreted by the mammary glands, will induce the attitude and behavior of mother love in female animals that have no young of their own, or sometimes even in males! Such instances could be multiplied many times.

Though the detailed physiological basis of our motives has only begun to be explored, we can discover much about them without it, says the psychologist, and learn to manipulate them just as we can learn to drive a car without understanding all the mechanical principles on which it runs. But as we know that the successful action of switches, gears, and pistons in the operation of a car depends upon the principles of physics and thermodynamics, and that these sciences must be mastered if we are really to understand what makes the car go, so a complete knowledge of the body as a dynamic system will be necessary if we are to master the final secrets of its behavior.

The way is now open, says the physiological psychologist, for an analysis of the motives that make us act the way we do. The mechanics of the directive process are little by little becoming clearer. We are beginning to understand, so to speak, how the carburetor and the timer are adjusted, how the throttle works, and the function of the spark plugs. These are notable accomplishments and promise others greater still. But beneath all this, one must admit, there remains the unsolved problem of what turns the steering wheel and what depresses the accelerator. Why do some human machines move in this direction and others in that? Why do some wander aimlessly along the roads of life while their colleagues of the same make and model drive steadily and straight to a particular destination? Why do some develop a flood of spiritual horsepower and others use their fuel inefficiently? These problems, say the adherents of the mechanistic conception of our motives, are indeed most difficult but we can be assured that they will reach solution as knowledge grows. Psychology is only at the threshold, and under the tremendous stimulus of these new ideas its future progress toward an understanding of behavior will be almost limitless.

For a psychology thus based on biology the term "motive" is an appropriate one. Motive is to be thought of simply as the power that moves an individual with a certain force. Psychology now interprets all motives as drives, rooted in man's living protoplasmic system and thus based finally on physiological necessity. Through the continued action of natural selection the behavior that results from such drives will tend to insure the survival of the individual.

Hunger, for example, is a powerful drive, an expression of the requirement of a continual supply of food that will provide energy to run the bodily machine and material for its repair and growth. Water is necessary for the body's welfare too, and its procurement results from the drive of thirst. Both these are manifestations of that "wisdom of the body" without which life could not long survive. To escape from pain is another useful drive that tends toward health and safety. Injury and illness would take a far heavier toll than now they do were we not strongly moved to remedy them by seeking relief from the various pains they cause. The sex drive has an obvious biological basis. Upon its vigorous expression the survival of a species must finally depend, for it insures the production of new individuals to take the place of those that are lost by death. Modern psychology, particularly of the Freudian school, places great emphasis on the importance of this drive as underlying much of human behavior. Its influence, direct or indirect, is very great.

There are other motives that have physiological foundations, though often less evident ones. Among these are the emotions, in which we are moved to fear, anger, love, hate, joy, anguish, and the like. Feelings of pleasure, at least in their simplest forms, arise from the satisfaction of biological drives, and unpleasant ones from their frustration. Such motives seem to be of value for survival and to have developed in the course of man's long evolution. Thus anger increases the body's physical powers, and fear lends speed to the feet. Other emotions have risen far higher than their origin and are among the most satisfying of human experiences.

Above the obviously biological level too are motives like personal ambition; the pursuit of wealth, power, and prestige; the eagerness for adventure; or an urge for creative activity. Many of these may be called "social" motives, since they distinguish a particular culture and have been acquired in it. Much of what is often thought to be instinctive behavior has thus come from the social environment in which a person has been reared. The need for security is a powerful drive in producing the development of groups, for example, and from this, in turn, is patriotism born.

Every modern textbook of psychology devotes many of

its pages to the problem of motives. We are told how the frustration of a drive may lead to its expression in other ways, as when the sex urge, blocked in its normal course, may be "sublimated" to a love for all mankind. Sometimes, on the contrary, frustration leads to violent and aggressive behavior. The Freudians maintain that many motives are rooted in early attitudes, notably that of a child toward its parent of the opposite sex. Other hidden roots of consciousness have been explored, and we have learned that there are springs of motivation, often unrecognized, that flow from early experiences and conditioning. Search for them is an important part of the practice of psychiatry.

The psychologist is interested in origins, not in ends; in sources, not in destinations; in driving forces, not in drawing power. Surely, he says, the motives for a man's acts arise from the physical state of his brain and not from any tenuous and indefinable "purpose" that he holds. We have outgrown this old idea. To assume that such a thing as purpose is effective seems to him sheer mysticism, a resurrection of the old, vexed question of "final" causes and teleology, which science long ago discarded and laid decently to rest.

Goals as Motives

It is here, however, that the modern science of the mind leaves many with an uncomfortable sense of insufficiency, a feeling that something important has been overlooked, a vital part of man left out of the picture because it somehow does not fit into a theory. The common attitude of men is forward-looking, purposeful. Goal-seekers all men are. What gives to life its meaning and its flavor is the pursuit of something much desired. To deny this is to violate a deeply seated conviction. Whatever the psychologist may say, we do not *feel* as if we were impelled by forces from behind or driven to a destination, as if our motives were the push and thrust of a machine propelling us onward. Sometimes, indeed, men do appear to be caught up by a power they are unable to resist, and driven about like victims of the Furies in a Greek tragedy; but far more commonly we feel ourselves not driven thus but rather pulled or drawn *toward* something yet unrealized, a purpose, goal, or aspiration, something to be achieved in the uncertain future. Our motivation seems to be the tug exerted by these goals of our desire, not the push of physical necessity. How "drive" can be translated to "desire" remains a difficult problem for psychology.

Common experience looks on the idea that we are pushed about by such inner drives as unreal and artificial. What meaning can it have, we say, for men whose lives are dedicated to the pursuit of knowledge or the creation of beauty or the service of their fellows? What place in it is there for devotion and sacrifice and that endless striving for truth and human betterment which ever has distinguished man at his best? How can it satisfy all those who have burning in their hearts the flame of divine discontent that lifts men higher than the beasts? Men seem not to be pushed into the finest things they do but to follow the urgent call of something that draws them on through hardship and uncertainty and discouragement to the attainment of a high desire. If powerful motives such as these are but illusions, then indeed have we been much deceived. As L. J. Henderson once remarked of consciousness that it "cannot be regarded as merely a useless by-product of the evolutionary process," so one might well say that goal-seeking, seemingly so powerful in the life of man, cannot be regarded as a mere by-product of metabolism.

Psychology is bound to feel somewhat embarrassed over this dilemma between science and common sense. It cannot discount the importance of man's conviction that he eagerly seeks the ends for which he longs, and mechanistic psychology must either interpret these feelings as illusions with no real validity, or else, by granting him freedom to pursue his ends, it must abandon the concept of determinism and predictability in nature. Here is the ancient dilemma between fate and freedom that has troubled philosophers and common men from ancient times to our own day. To choose between its horns seems to require the violation of one or the other of our deep convictions.

Whatever our belief may be as to the ultimate nature of the universe and of our relation to it, these curious qualities of man, these goals and dreams and aspirations, are worthy of much further exploration. We should not be tempted to neglect them because they do not fit precisely into present scientific ideology. These things exist. They are involved in everything we do, and it cannot be denied that they are the most distinctive elements in the character of everyone. Man may be regarded as a material system, driven by physical forces, as biology assumes; but he may also be thought of as being drawn on by purpose and desire. Development of the former concept has helped to discover a vast deal about him, but the latter, if diligently followed without prejudice, may reveal still more.

The conception of the relation between body and mind presented in these pages has the advantage of avoiding, at least in part, the dilemma of motivation we have been discussing. Neither horn need be discarded. The concept simply assumes that purpose and desire are the inner experience of that tendency toward self-regulation and goal-seeking that distinguishes all organic activity, bodily or mental. The tension, the pull, of this regulation is *felt* and need not be explained away as fiction or illusion. It is a very real fact. As to the actual mechanism of this regulation, of how these protoplasmic goals are set up, toward which both growth and behavior conform, our theory has nothing to say. It simply interprets mind and motives on the basis of a quality of living stuff that can be demonstrated though not yet clearly understood. Attempts at explaining it may be as strictly mechanistic as one pleases and need involve no sacrifice of a belief in the uniformity of nature, no commitment to vitalism or to mysticism. There must obviously be a close relation between a purpose in the mind and its physical basis in the body; but just what a goal or purpose actually is in terms of matter and energy will depend at last, I think, on what the physical basis of biological self-regulation finally turns out to be.

This conception has the advantage over present psychological orthodoxy in that its attitude is forward, *toward* a goal to be reached, and not back to the push and drive of circumstance, and is thus in harmony with the common verdict of experience. This, I repeat, implies no "final" cause but simply the conformity of behavior to a norm or goal set up in the living system. One school of psychology in the late nineteenth century, that of Brentano, frankly accepted the concept of *intention* as fundamental. This, to be sure, was before the modern ideas of neuro-physiology were very far advanced. Brentano's position had the advantage of turning psychology to the future. Professor Gordon Allport, to whom I am indebted for a knowledge of Brentano, well describes the present difficulty of his science in this regard. Says he: "The chief shortcoming of American psychology up to now, I think, is its poverty in representing the future.

While most people are absorbed in planning for, working for, dreaming for, the future, psychology for the most part is busily engaged in tracing their lives backward. Most psychologists see behavior as pushed 'from behind' by goads that prod us out of our past. Yet is it not characteristic of maturely directed activity, arising from the sentiments that form personality, that it is always oriented toward the future? To understand a person we have to know what he is trying to accomplish, what he is trying to become, not merely 'how he got the way he is.' . . . All people are in transit; and we find it less revealing to know where they came from or where they are now than to know their in-intended destinations." [1] With this point of view our present suggestion is in close agreement.

But let us return again to the practical side of the matter. What difference does it make in accounting for human motives whether we choose the alternative of drive or of draw, of a compulsion with its roots in physiology or of a protoplasmic purpose growing from self-regulation? There is a very real difference here. If we accept desires, goals, purposes, and intentions as real and effective, as part of the data of the universe, though yet we do not understand their origin, we can develop better methods, I believe, for guiding man's behavior than we can if we think of him as driven along his course—better because they are in closer harmony with his real nature. For all who are seeking to improve society it thus becomes a task of major consequence to find how these elusive qualities may be called forth and how they may so be elevated as to draw men upward in achieving them. Whatever theory of motivation one adopts, this

[1] *The Individual and His Religion* (New York: The Macmillan Company, 1950), p. 129.

task deserves more emphasis than it has received, and for those who look on goals as primary factors in behavior, it is paramount.

Guiding Man's Conduct

Unless behavior conforms to certain general moral patterns, men cannot live successfully together. To make it so conform, and thus to preserve society from disintegration, dependence in the past has been on two chief means—the law, and the rational persuasions of education and the intellect. Men have been forced to do right and taught what is right to do. Neither means has proven a complete success, nor ever will, I fear, unless their service is supplemented by an elevation of men's motives. It is here that the interpretation of behavior as rooted in the purposiveness of all life may prove of service.

Law in enlightened societies is the result of long experience in dealing with men—"the last result," said Dr. Johnson, "of human wisdom acting upon human experience." It is simply an attempt on a grand scale to substitute right for might by reasonable means. Laws are of great service in providing a code of rules to control human relations and in enforcing obedience to them. The majesty of the law is a noble concept, and where it is supported by powerful sanctions and by public opinion it is greatly effective in controlling men's actions. A democracy prides itself on being a government of laws, not men. Despite all this, we sadly must admit today that the law is far from successful in accomplishing its purposes. Courts and police and prisons take an ever larger share of society's resources. Crime and delinquency are rampant. As a mechanically minded folk, we turn instinctively to legal machinery for the remedy of

our ills, but often enough we have learned that morality
cannot be gained by law alone. You cannot legislate men
into righteousness.

Beyond the realm of laws made and enforced by the state
rises the edifice of moral law, looked on by many as part of
the system of natural law by which the universe is governed.
Every great religion has its moral laws, and obedience to
them is the basis of the conduct it requires from all its fol-
lowers. In the Hebrew tradition, especially, the Law is sacred
and supreme, and much of this attitude has been retained
in Christianity. The commandments of God, however, even
when their authority is freely acknowledged, are as often
disobeyed as those of man. Laws are essential, one readily
admits, and without them society could not survive; but
they depend at last on compulsion for their success, and
force is not the final answer to the problem of how to make
men live together in constructive peace and harmony. Fear
of hell or the hangman has doubtless kept many a distracted
soul from crime, but it will take much more than fear of
these to build the good society. Virtue must grow inwardly.
To impose it from without may gain temporary success but
almost always ends in final failure.

For those who seek to turn men's paths to virtue, the second method, education, seems to be more promising. Plato
once said that to know the right is to do it. If one really
knows what the right is, what is best for himself and for
others, what the universal experience of the race approves,
it seems obvious that he then will follow it in his behavior.
Many indeed are thus guided by reason, convinced that in
the long run it is the best course to follow. Surely there must
be a reasonable basis for our morals. Ethical conduct is
rooted in reason as well as in the Ten Commandments.
Theft, murder, and war are not only immoral but irrational,

and reason alone, we are likely to say, ought to be enough to conquer them.

But in the hour of grievous temptation reason is a slender reed on which to lean. As Adam found to his sorrow, eating of the tree of the *knowledge* of good and evil by no means guarantees that one will choose the good. Man prides himself on being a rational creature, but he often acts irrationally. It is surprising and humiliating to him to find that his deeds so often go directly contrary to what reason tells him. As St. Paul ruefully remarked, "The good that I would I do not, but the evil which I would not, that I do." An inner compulsion draws us—call it original sin, or the Devil, or human nature, or simply strong determination and desire. It is the same sort of thing that draws us to beauty and good deeds, a stronger attraction than the voice of reason alone.

How much more certain a man is to do right if he not only knows what it is but *wants* to do it! This want guards him far more strongly against wrong than does the enforcement of his loyalty by law or obligation. A strong desire, a goal he seeks, is more powerful in the end than these. The lesson we must learn is that the only sure way to make man moral is through his motives, to make him *want* to do the things he *ought* to do. The means to save society may be as simple—and as difficult—as that. What makes us do evil is that evil, for one reason or another, attracts us more than good does. Not until virtue is attractive *for its own sake* will men cleave always to it. Our motives, our emotions, our *movings* must be elevated if life is to reach a higher moral plane. Many reformers think that emotions are a hindrance to man's attainment of the ideal society, and look forward to the day when reason only, unclouded by feeling, will guide his conduct. That day will never come, for emotion gives the motive power for behavior. Says a modern text, "Man is primarily a creature of impulse, wanting, demanding, fearing, loving, and hating; he is only secondarily a creature of intelligence and reason." [2] Science can help develop techniques by which the good life can be found, but we shall never attain to it unless we earnestly *desire* to do so.

This does not mean, of course, that education is not a powerful factor in determining what our motives come to be, or that reason is not important for morality. One will hardly do right unless he gains a knowledge of what it is. But education only digs the channel, so to speak, along which the river of life may flow. Too often it shoves and pushes a reluctant pupil on, instead of setting before him a goal so attractive and compelling that he moves forward toward it by his own efforts. The two conceptions of motivation, although their techniques may often be the same, are different in their fundamental attitudes. Education tends too frequently to be pedestrian, plodding along the road of learning and filling the student's mind with many kinds of knowledge. All this is valuable and necessary, for each generation must stand on the shoulders of its predecessors and learn from the records of their experience. But education has often failed in a task no less important—to elevate the youthful goals and ambitions that provide the motive power for life. It hangs up too few stars to which youngsters can hitch their wagons. It promotes virtue through precept rather than through preference. It cultivates ideas but lets ideals grow as they will. "Ideals are like stars," Carl Schurz once said. "You will not succeed in touching them with your

[2] Ross Stagner and T. F. Karwoski, *Psychology* (New York: McGraw-Hill Company, 1952), p. 8.

hands. But like the seafaring man on the desert of waters, you choose them as your guides, and following them you will reach your destiny."

In the light of all this, how shall we proceed to help men nourish loftier desires and lift their aspirations higher? How can we set up worthier goals within their minds? The psychologist knows some of the techniques by which men's motives may be guided. Early conditioning and education are the most important of these, and the highest hope for man, he says, must lie in using them for the training of our youth. Means for doing this are even now at hand, and by wisely employing them we shall learn to control more skillfully what men do, and thus make possible a better world.

We shall do well to listen to all that the psychologist, with his wide experience in such matters, has to tell us. But his emphasis on drives, as we have seen, does not seem to strike squarely at the center of the problem we are facing here. How can one learn to want something? Goal-seeking is universal at all biological levels, but the goals sought often can be greatly modified.

In an attempt to change the course of man's desires it is worth while to observe the steps by which they normally come into being. First, among the welter of impressions and experiences, something attracts attention and arouses interest. As the psychologists say, the mind has a "set" toward it. If it can be possessed or experienced, interest in it often enlarges to desire. Should this persist and conditions make it possible, desire may grow to purpose or intention, and these, in turn, to longing and determination. However one interprets human motives, this hierarchy is evident within them.

The obvious first step is to draw attention to the thing or quality one is trying to build into a goal, to bring it vividly into consciousness and awaken interest in it. How *do* you go about interesting yourself or someone else in a specific thing? How does a parent do it for his child? Merely to offer something and to say, "This should be fun; you ought to like it," will not be enough. Perhaps the very fact that you urge him to accept it will prevent his doing so. The approach must usually be more indirect. If the youngster is put into an environment where a particular activity or value is emphasized, where others are keenly interested in it, and where the paraphernalia for it are at hand, it will of necessity occupy an important place in his attention. This, and the almost irrepressible human tendency to imitate, will in many cases be enough to awaken interest. The contagion of intimacy can be counted on to do its work.

Boyhood is full of such contagions, often fleeting, but powerful while they last. One year stamp collecting may be spreading like wildfire through the youthful community, with almost everybody poring over catalogs, immersed in albums and "approval sheets," buying, swapping, dreaming. Another time it may be flying kites, or collecting beetles, or hunting Indian arrowheads. Often these enthusiasms lead to the first deep yearnings of life, the first emotional stirrings of longing or ambition.

Sometimes these early interests persist and grow into the goal-seeking of maturer years. These too are largely determined by the sort of things with which we come into daily contact, the concerns of our friends and neighbors, their values and goals—in short, the culture pattern of the particular society in which we live. It is natural—almost inevitable—that in New England people should be interested in antique furniture and ancient houses, that Canadians should be enthusiasts for winter sports, or that a fisherman's son should share his father's love for rod and fly.

By a deliberate act of choice one may turn his attention to a particular subject or activity, may put it in the forefront of his mind from time to time and live with it. He may turn his steps once a week to an art museum or consciously direct his reading to some chosen field. He may begin to indulge the universal human love of collecting something. If he enters such an activity through choice, with the deliberate intent of being pleasantly ensnared thereby, he almost certainly will succeed. In the cultivation of more serious goals the same technique will often be an aid. If one consciously fills his mind with a goal, the time will soon arrive when deliberate effort of attention is no longer necessary, for the compass-needle of his heart swings naturally toward its new pole. St. Paul's wise admonition is still worth attending by all who seek to cultivate high ideals: "Whatsoever things are true, whatsoever things are honest, whatsoever things are just, whatsoever things are pure, whatsoever things are lovely, whatsoever things are of good report; if there be any virtue, and if there be any praise, think on these things."

Deliberate attention is the first step necessary. But attention alone is often not enough. The ignition point at which interest will take fire to make the warmth of purpose is often so high that we cannot by ourselves generate the necessary heat to accomplish it. Desire and aspiration come oftener from something outside us, from the ideas and personalities of others. Exposure indeed is necessary, but active contagion is more often required.

This contagion may be one of ideas only. A book has often remade a life completely, as the Bible countless times has done. Ability to read it in the tongue of common speech aroused new hopes and aspirations in men and made the Reformation inevitable. Discovery of the great ideas of antiquity awakened new longings, and from these arose the Renaissance. Books and other forms of literature are far more than records of the past, repositories of knowledge, or means to delight our leisure. They preserve the great ideas and insights of earlier days, the accumulated wisdom of mankind. In them we have a reservoir from which to fill our souls, broaden our interests and desires, and lift our ideals beyond the levels we can reach ourselves. They should not merely instruct us. They should set us on fire!

But books too often lie undiscovered on the library shelves. To gain inspiration from them we must take the initiative. Reading is an art, and not everyone, however literate he may be, has mastered it. The written word is but the shadow of the spoken one. It is the living man, by the contagion not of his words alone but of his deeds and example, who through the ages has set other men ablaze and put in their hearts high aspirations they could never gain from any other source. Education at its best is such a process of intellectual contagion. A great teacher is not simply one who imparts knowledge to his students, but one who awakens their interest in it and makes them eager to pursue it for themselves. He is a spark plug, not a fuel pipe. The reason colleges exist is to bring students into contact with contagious personalities, for otherwise they might as well be correspondence schools.

Of the utmost importance also are the spiritual leaders of our race, the founders of the religions of the world and a host of their successors through the centuries, men who inspired their fellows and whose influence on the goals men seek has been profound. They have spoken to something deeper than reason, making men long for things that by themselves they never would have sought.

Such are some of the practical aspects of a philosophy that looks on goals, desires, and purposes as primary, not secondary, things; that seeks the origin of motives in something that draws a man, not drives him—something he wants; and that sees his wanting of it as an effective reality and not illusion. Such a conception can be defended by much evidence from biology, for it is in harmony with the essential quality of life, though its interpretation in terms of physical science is still far from clear. We should not let this hold us back, it seems to me, from using it as the foundation for our philosophy of behavior. Behavior is a biological process, not a chemical one only. From *Amoeba* to *Homo sapiens,* in all the complex systems it builds, protoplasm is a goal-seeker, and unless we take this carefully into account we shall find ourselves committing the error of treating organisms as far too simple things, and thus miss the vital core of what they are.

For psychology, and more especially for sociology and education, a recognition of this fact should be of great importance. Although it would not change immediately many of their aims and methods, the philosophy of motivation it presents, so different from the one in vogue today, would in the end profoundly influence not only our understanding of behavior but the means we employ to alter it. He who learns to remold the heart's desire, and not the mind's intent alone, will hold in his hands the key to our salvation.

CHAPTER V

The Philosophy of Goals

Abstract

What philosophical conclusions can be drawn from this idea of organic purposefulness?

It suggests that man's nature is not double, but that both body and mind are based on the regulatory and goal-seeking quality of living stuff. Whence this comes is first a problem for biology and is actively being studied by this science. Natural selection cannot well account for it. Mechanistic biology, though confident of explaining it finally in terms of physics and chemistry, as yet is far from doing so. To assume the operation of a localized entelechy or psychic factor here, as vitalism does, faces grave difficulties. Organicism recognizes the organizing, self-regulatory power of living stuff but cannot find a basis for it. To do so will probably require not only an exploration of radically new ideas in biology but perhaps even the adoption of new scientific concepts. The biologist is bound more and more to face problems biology must share with philosophy.

By its technique of analysis science has learned much about the material world and has broken it down into smaller and smaller particles. It finds that the continual shuffling of these particles tends toward disorganization and the "running down" of the universe. The presence of definite forms, however, as of atoms, crystals, and organisms, shows that there are also synthetic factors operating in nature. For science to deal with these is much more difficult. Self-regulation and purposiveness in a living organism pose such a problem of synthesis at the highest and most creative level, that of life. How goals are set up in protoplasm and how they operate there to control development and behavior we do not yet understand. We may have to postulate the operation in nature of "formative tendencies" at present unknown. Goal-seeking and directiveness in organisms should be recognized as a basic fact and life's most characteristic quality. About it center the great problems of biology and philosophy.

The concept we have been defending here is that all life is purposeful; that the development of an embryo, the growth of a conscious purpose in the mind, and the aspiration of the human spirit differ only in degree and are all manifestations of a basic goal-seeking quality characteristic of life at every level. To what conclusion, we may now ask, does all this lead? What sort of philosophy can be constructed from it?

The most important contribution it can offer, I think, is the one already emphasized, that dualism—the idea that man's nature is a double one, part body and part mind—is not a necessary concept. The problem with which our discussions began was whether these two parts of man cannot be reconciled. The answer we are now prepared to give is that they can be; that they are not fundamentally different, but simply two aspects of the self-regulating, goal-seeking, creative tendency all life displays. The body is its material product, the mind the controlled behavior that comes from it, and consciousness the experience we have of it. Man's basic unity is the unity of life.

Dualism has found distinguished sponsors from Aristotle's day to ours. Many philosophers have supported it. That man's immaterial portion has an existence in its own right is a reassuring faith and lends itself to the hopes and consolations of religion far better than the idea that he is simply a creature of the dust. The soul is a precious thing and not lightly to be tossed aside. But most of us are monists at heart and would like to think of the universe as made of one stuff, not two. Dualism is especially unpopular as a philosophy for science since it seems to imply mysticism, the supernatural, and the existence of disembodied spirits, with none of which science is prepared to deal. The alternative monistic philosophy, however, in its commonest form sees the universe as indeed a unity but a unity based only on matter, the final reality. It looks on mind as a by-product with no real existence of its own, something that is tied inexorably to physical processes and produced by them much as music is produced by a phonograph. The material part of man appears so permanent and stable that it seems to offer a more satisfactory basis for his life than the fluctuating and discontinuous existence of his "mind."

Such a mechanistic attitude has strong support today and is the orthodoxy of communism. It is the conclusion many scientists find most acceptable. It can easily be defended and may turn out to be the only theory in harmony with all the facts. If not only the metabolic processes of living things but their self-regulating character—the fact on which our hypothesis here rests—can finally be explained in terms of present-day mechanics and biochemistry, the materialistic interpretation of life will be vindicated, and everything will be proved to have its origin in matter and energy. This idea need not have the dreary overtones that materialism has often gathered about itself, for matter as it is pictured by modern physics has now lost the rigid and mechanical character it once was thought to possess and may have leeway enough in its behavior to allow for freedom and creativeness. Matter is nothing but energy, and its ultimate course may be unpredictable. After all, our bodies are material systems and made of the same elements that form the substance of the earth and of the farthest stars. Matter doubtless holds more possibilities than we can dream of now. We should heed Emerson's admonition to "make friends with matter, which the ambitious chatter of the schools would persuade us to despise. We never can part with it; the mind loves its old home: as water to our thirst, so is the rock, the ground to our eyes, and hands, and feet." [1]

Despite all such fine words matter still is matter, and a philosophy based upon it runs so counter to man's deepest convictions that it seems unlikely ever to prove satisfying for most people. The concept we have here been advocating not only avoids the dualistic view of man but in addition has an advantage over this materialistic sort of monism in not being committed to either body or mind as the essential reality, since it regards *both* as derived from something deeper than either. What this something is, which thus becomes the source of body, mind, and spirit, is the final problem. Upon our answer to it will depend the sort of philosophy we must construct.

At the biological level this problem is to find an explanation for the fact of self-regulation, the universal tendency, in development and physiological activity, to move toward the attainment and maintenance of a specific goal. What is

[1] Ralph Waldo Emerson in his essay on "Nature."

the source of this remarkable trait in living things? For many years this has been the subject of active experiment and speculation. Great progress has been made in a knowledge of just what the changes are in cells and their constituents, in chemical substances and physical relations, which occur as an organism grows, and are especially evident when the course of its normal development is upset. The altering potencies of growing structures and the ways in which differences arise among them have been examined. There are encouraging results from explorations on the roles of many specific agencies and substances involved in embryology; and about some of these, notably genes, hormones, and various stimulators and inhibitors of growth, much is already known. What controls them, however, so that just the right amount is present at the right time and place, what regulates the developing system and holds it together as an organism against the disorganizing tendencies in lifeless matter, is still unknown. Here lies the great enigma of biology. Ingenious hypotheses of many sorts have been proposed, but none has pierced to the center of the problem or won wide acceptance. The organism has been analyzed with increasing precision into ever smaller bits and processes, but how from these an organized and living whole arises still eludes us.

Self-Regulation and Natural Selection

The evolutionist, however, has a suggestion here. Self-regulation, he says, is obviously advantageous. It restores lost or injured parts, maintains the organism's physical equilibrium, and in general keeps it going. Like all such useful traits in living things, it must have arisen through natural selection. Those individuals in which it was best developed had an advantage over their competitors, survived, and passed this trait on to their descendants. There is nothing more mysterious about self-regulation than there is about any other organic character.

This explanation, I think, is open to serious objection. In the first place, ability to regenerate lost parts is difficult to account for through natural selection since in most species a need for it would rarely be met. In nature there are few occasions when the ability of an isolated piece of stem to restore a root system, for example, would be called upon, and it is difficult to believe that this widespread ability has arisen through competitive selection. Furthermore, the most remarkable cases of regeneration, such as the growth of a whole tadpole from one of the first two cells of a frog embryo, or the reintegration of a sponge from its many scrambled cells, could have been discovered only by laboratory experiments and would almost never have occurred in nature.

Another argument against this idea is that the specific shapes of tissue and organ so characteristic of living things, which are the most obvious result of organized and regulated growth, seem rarely to be of value in evolution. In many cases—perhaps most—what favors survival seems rather an inherent toughness and adaptability, or success in producing many offspring. Can we imagine, for example, that the differences in leaf shape among our various species of maples and oaks have a great deal to do with the evolutionary success of these species? This success is rooted in something deeper, but it is these relatively unimportant shape differences that result from the regulated development we have been discussing. Surely natural selection can hardly be invoked to explain such regulation.

It must be recognized, of course, that organization occurs

at many levels, and that in the higher ones part of it may
be disturbed or even destroyed. In tumors or other types
of abnormal growth, for example, the control that holds the
organism together as an integrated system has been broken
down. This is even more evident in tissue culture, where
cells or bits of tissue may be made to grow indefinitely
without showing any phenomena of organization above the
cellular level. These cells are alive and active, however,
though they have lost the capacity to build an organism.
This does not mean that the basic organizing control over
cellular metabolism and growth at this *lowest* level is not
as active as ever. Without it, life would cease. Indeed, some
self-regulation, though at different levels and to different
degrees and subject to partial loss, seems present everywhere in living things and is an essential characteristic of
life itself. Life *is* a state of dynamic equilibrium in which
the organism, like a man walking on a tightrope, is continually adjusting itself to external circumstances. The constant
physiological conditions it maintains and the precise forms
it develops are the result of this. Without regulation life
would not be life. In considering the origin of self-regulation, we therefore are not dealing with the sort of trait that
has been developed by natural selection—such as a bird's
ability to fly or the adaptation of flowers to insect pollina-
tion—but with a fundamental quality of all life.

Whether or not life arose by anything comparable to
natural selection—perhaps among various types of protein
molecules—we cannot say, but this seems very doubtful;
and the origin of life at all events is still entirely unknown.
In its basic qualities, however, it seems to have changed
little in countless millions of years, for protoplasm, its
physical foundation, is much the same through the whole
evolutionary series from microbes to man. To understand

self-regulation, therefore, would mean not only solving this particular problem but reaching the final and far more difficult goal of understanding the origin and innermost nature of life itself.

Mechanism, Vitalism, and Organicism

The unifying, self-regulating quality of life must evidently have its basis in protoplasm, and the argument here soon centers in the question of what this material is and what goes on within it.

To this the mechanistic biologist has an immediate and very definite answer. Nothing occurs in protoplasm that is fundamentally different from the processes we know already in inorganic systems. Every activity of life will ultimately be found to have its basis in chemical changes in this living stuff. In support of his conclusion he points to the rapid progress that is being made toward an understanding of many vital activities, notably in metabolism. Respiration, for example, has been shown to be far more complex than a mere taking in of oxygen and giving off of carbon dioxide and water. It consists of a fantastically complex series of steps involving many chemical changes, each produced by a specific enzyme. These changes all seem to be perfectly understandable chemistry and to involve nothing mysterious or "vital." Such investigation of protoplasmic activities is proceeding rapidly and meeting with very great success. Many biochemists are confident that by this means it will in time be possible to analyze the other vital processes and find at last a chemical basis for life.

Despite all this, living stuff is so different—not in chemical constitution but in its behavior and organization—from matter in a lifeless state that many have often wondered whether in living systems there may not be something radically different from what is found in the lifeless universe outside them. As "vitalism" this idea has been upheld in modern times by only a few biologists. It has generally assumed that in every organism there is something in the nature of a director or guide or entelechy, a sort of psychic factor that somehow interjects itself, particularly at critical times, to keep the organism unified and to overcome the disruptive tendencies dead matter inevitably displays. Just how this operates is difficult to imagine, and this difficulty has led most biologists to deny the truth of vitalism entirely. That anything can upset the strict determinism of physical events so violates the canons of scientific orthodoxy that it has become an almost disreputable idea. Ralph Lillie has discussed this problem ably and at length as it is related to biological organization, teleology, and the nature of the mind. He maintains that a psychic factor of some sort *must* affect physical events, since this is a universal experience of mankind and should be regarded as experimentally established. As a tentative explanation he invokes the statistical concept of natural law and suggests that the psychic factor operates by shifting the *probability* of events, especially on the scale of quanta and very minute particles, so that instead of their moving entirely at random, they have a slight preponderance in a specific direction. Just where this effect is produced is, of course, the critical question. Lillie suggests that "the factors underlying psychical action have a certain *inner* or non-spatial quality which places them on a different plane from the plane of purely physical action, meaning here by 'physical action' any action forming part of an external or spatial world and describable in terms of external observation. Psychical factors, according to this view, would have a non-spatial, or form part of a non-spatial, mode of existence." [2] Driesch and other vitalists have also suggested an explanation much like this.

The difficulties of such a vitalistic conception are obvious and to many seem insuperable. Aside from offering no basis for experimental attack on the problem—so far as we can see—it seems to introduce an arbitrary element into the government of living things. Most people are convinced as a matter of common sense and undeniable experience that "mind" does somehow affect physical events; but to imagine this as being accomplished by an operator in the brain who from time to time, by a slight touch on the steering mechanism, changes the course of things, thus injecting mind into the affairs of matter, seems but a clumsy and ignoble conception both of life and man. In this most profound and personal relationship between ourselves and the forces of nature we should like to think that something more universal is at work than a little switchman concealed in the depths of the machinery.

What position should the biologist take today if he wishes to avoid that dilemma the horns of which are vitalism and mechanism? The most familiar solution of this difficulty is to adopt the position commonly called "organicism," which is simply a recognition of the fact that living stuff has the remarkable organizing capacities which the student of development has demonstrated. This is little more, however, than admission that the problem exists. The organicist is bound, I think, to be agnostic in his biology in that he simply does not know whence this strange organizing power arises. Clothing his ignorance with words will prove of little use in finding what we seek, the common origin of man's

[2] Ralph S. Lillie, *General Biology and Philosophy of Organism* (Chicago: University of Chicago Press, 1945), p. 130.

whole nature—body, mind, and spirit—in the processes of life.

It is here that the hypothesis we have been trying to develop offers a more satisfactory alternative. Something there surely is in any living thing which pulls dead, random matter into the form of an organized individual and holds it steadily there through material flux and change. The moment death occurs a radical alteration takes place, for this integrating force is gone and the bodily materials at once begin to break up into randomness again. This organizing power is life's peculiar quality. It never seems to arise spontaneously but is passed along from one organism to its offspring in a kind of apostolic succession, without a break.

This power *as a general property of life,* and not as the result of localized entelechies or directive agents, is therefore, it seems to me, the basic problem. We must admit that our ignorance about it is essentially complete. There are two positions in this difficult matter, however, that should be avoided. One is that the problem is insoluble and that no rational inquiry into it is possible. The other is to maintain, in the face of all the evidence of experience to the contrary, that a living organism is no different in character from a lifeless physico-chemical mechanism, and that mind as a directive factor is inconceivable. A more reasonable attitude to take is neither that of tender-minded vitalism nor tough-minded mechanism, but rather what might well be called biological agnosticism, a recognition that in living things there are facts we must accept but cannot yet by any means explain, a confession of ignorance but by no means an admission that the final problem must forever be insoluble. It would be foolish, I believe, to think that the present concepts of biology cannot be modified or that radically new facts about life will not sometime be discovered. The experience of physics in the past half-century should warn us that science has by no means yet exhausted its exploration of avenues to an understanding of the universe. What, for example, may come of further investigation of bio-electrical fields in living things, or of the field theory in general as applied to biology? Such a concept, with its idea of a constant spatial pattern of force that governs the distribution of particles, suggests the pattern of an organism. Attention, too, has often been called to the analogies between the nervous system and the operation of an electronic calculator, with its feed-back mechanism and other details that suggest organic controls and may, indeed, lead to a clearer understanding of biological activities. Von Bertalanffy and others are developing what they call a General Systems Theory, which endeavors to understand living systems *as such*.

It seems more probable, however, that radically new ways of looking at nature may have to be opened, ways that are so different from the familiar ones science long has trod that many will refuse to recognize them. What are we to say, for example, to the abundant evidence that telepathy is a fact and that other fields of what is called parapsychology deal with real phenomena and not imaginary ones? These ideas so completely violate accepted canons that few psychologists are willing even to consider the possibility that they may be true. No mechanism has yet been found by which such phenomena may be analyzed or explained in familiar terms. Radically different views as to the nature of space and time may have to be developed to deal with phenomena like these, and the theory of relativity has made a beginning at this difficult task. Scientists brought up in the older modes of thinking will hardly blaze fresh trails here, and the establishment of new ideas may have to await the passing of their opponents from the scene.

Try as he will, the biologist is bound to confront metaphysical problems, as the physicist is already doing. He now is likely to throw up his hands and cry that such ideas are outside the boundaries of science and thus are no concern of his; but unless we define science very narrowly it will have sufficient latitude to take in frontier problems such as these. It surely behooves the biologist to think far enough into these difficult matters so that he can reach an intelligent understanding of what the problems are. The physicist is devoting much attention to such questions as the nature of physical reality, the mathematician to the relations of space and time, and the cosmogonist to the origin and destiny of the universe. In such explorations as these the biologist is bound sooner or later to have an important share. His material is so much more complex than that with which the physical scientists work that he will necessarily lag somewhat behind them, but in the end he will have much to say about philosophical problems. Indeed, it may be that the biologist, dealing as he does with far more complex phenomena of physics and chemistry than do physical scientists, will in the end be able to demonstrate qualities in matter and energy that could never be discovered except by studying them in their living state. J. S. Haldane once said, "All true knowledge must be a gradual revelation of the lower or more abstract in terms of the higher or more concrete aspects of reality; and as the conception of organism is a higher and more concrete conception than that of matter and energy, science must ultimately aim at gradually interpreting the physical world of matter and energy in terms of the biological conception of organism." [3]

[3] *Mechanism, Life and Personality* (New York: Dutton, 1914), p. 98.

Analysis and Synthesis

The scientist has blazed a wide trail into this tangled jungle of problems, though not into its very depths. His success in learning the secrets of the universe has been due in large measure to the most important of his methods, analysis. He breaks down his material into smaller and smaller pieces and thus divides to conquer. Modern biology began with the discovery that every individual is composed of tiny living units, the cells. Further analysis showed that the essential part of each cell is the nucleus, and within the nucleus were found the chromosomes. In the chromosomes are genes, each apparently a large protein molecule. Molecules are composed of atoms, and in atoms there are various "ultimate" particles—electrons, protons, mesons, and many more. Even energy is broken up into tiny units or quanta.

The continual aimless shuffling of physical particles tends to increase their randomness and to distribute them more evenly. As a result of this, says physics, the universe is steadily "running down"; its complex structures are disintegrating, and it is moving toward a state where all its material will be evenly dispersed and at the same temperature—a static death.

This drift toward disorganization has by no means broken nature down into uniformity, however, for in the world around us there are hosts of objects that are by no means random in their character. The simplest sort are those that show a definite relation between their parts and thus possess a form or pattern. This may be evident in external shape or in internal structure. In all such objects—crystals, clouds, trees, rocks, or animals—form has been impressed on formless, random matter. In the concern of science with analysis and its emphasis on unitary particles and their behavior, it has tended to lose sight of the processes of synthesis that produce form. In its preoccupation with the dancing, shuffling atoms, it has too much neglected how these particles actually behave. There must be forces that counteract the disorganizing ones we have described. Form is everywhere, and its significance has been pondered by thinkers from Aristotle to Goethe, Bergson, and Whitehead. Its importance has recently been emphasized anew by Whyte. "Beneath the apparently haphazard motions of particles," says he, "may lie a formative tendency toward simplicity of form, order and regularity." He suggests that "laws express the changes in whole patterns and cannot be expressed in terms of properties of single parts. . . . The only role of particles may be to mark and anchor patterns." [4] Form makes the particles, not particles the form.

The advantage of the analyst is obvious, for to dissect an object is far simpler than to find what formed it. Any youngster can take the mechanism of a clock apart, but to put it together again requires much skill. For this reason, doubtless, the analyzers, from Democritus and Newton to the atomic physicists of today, have been more successful than the synthesizers. The latter, to be sure, have framed many hypotheses. Whitehead regarded atoms as minute organisms. Karl Heim believes that a "wholeness tendency" must have a position of primacy in our philosophy. Whyte assumes a formativeness in nature. Others read there the designs of Universal Mind. L. J. Henderson believes that organization is a major category in nature, standing beside matter and energy. It is hard to subject such ideas to scientific study. They are difficult to take hold of, to test and measure.

[4] Lancelot Law Whyte, *Accent on Form* (New York: Harper and Brothers, 1954) , pp. 67, 63.

It is here that we come back to the problems that occupy the earlier chapters of this book. Are *all* forms, it now may be asked, evidence of purposive organization, of goal-seeking, or should we distinguish between inorganic and organic ones? Many philosophers are inclined to see a gradual transition between the simple, lifeless patterns of atom and crystal and the more complex ones of living things. A hydrogen atom with its single electron spinning around a nucleus is in a sense an organized system. In atoms with more electrons, the orbit of each has a definite relation to those of the others, and the organization is thus more complex. Whitehead saw no sharp distinction between these simple systems and far more complex ones, and was inclined to regard physics as the science that deals with minute organisms and biology as that which deals with larger ones. Molecules are patterned complexes of atoms, some of which can organize themselves into crystals possessing the most specific and constant forms in nature, almost limitless in number and variety. A crystal grows by the selective addition at its surface of particular kinds of molecules from its environment. It may even repair a broken portion of itself. No wonder that many have compared crystals to living organisms and have seen the same "formative tendency" in both. Some viruses may exist for long periods in "crystalline" form.

If this organic formativeness is essentially like that in living organisms, the basis for purposiveness and mind may exist far down in the lifeless world. *All* objects may thus have within them something of the psychical, as the philosophy of panpsychism maintains.

There is good reason, however, to believe that the sort of formativeness found in living things is really different from that in such lifeless ones as crystals. First, the crystal system is static. Its molecules are at rest. Whatever change there is results from the addition of new molecules along the crystal surface. A living organism, on the contrary, is in a continual state of change. Matter enters it and leaves it in a steady procession, and all sorts of processes go on within its cells. Unlike the rigid crystal, protoplasm is fluid in character. Despite this, the organism maintains its specific form —not as constant, to be sure, as that of a crystal, where all the faces and angles are determined with mathematical exactitude, but still so constant a pattern that each of the million kinds of living things may be recognized by its particular outer form and inner structure. An organism has a sort of fluid form like that of a waterfall, through which water ceaselessly is pouring but which keeps in its descent a definite pattern. The crystal's form results from the way its molecules are fitted tightly together, like pieces in a jigsaw puzzle; an organism's results from forces that control the molecules' fluid interactions and relations.

A second difference between crystal and organism is that crystals, like lifeless patterns generally, are fixed and changeless, whereas living things are changeful and creative. A crystal of sodium chloride two billion years ago was the same in form and structure, we are convinced, as is one today. Meanwhile the living world has arisen to its present high estate. To evolve is a trait of life, not of lifelessness. New things appear in life. Variation is the constant rule of living nature, and thence has come the upward course of evolutionary change with its high promise for the future.

Life Is the Final Problem

This fluidity and creativeness is so distinctive of organic forms and so unlike lifeless ones that we are justified, it seems to me, in regarding the two types as radically different from each other. A formative tendency that opposes randomness and produces atoms and crystals may be the dim beginning of the sort of formativeness that makes living things, but the two are very far apart. Only when we deal with the particular physical system that is protoplasm does the strange and unexplained phenomenon of life appear. How it arose we now have no idea. The fact that it comes only through the touch of pre-existing protoplasm and that life thus seems to be one vast, continuous web that reaches back into the dawn of things must have some meaning.

What organizes matter thus we do not know. Perhaps, as many think, when molecules of carbon compounds grew large enough and complex enough they automatically became endowed with properties of life. However this may be, there is something in life that produces harmony and pattern in a material system and keeps it moving toward a definite end. In observing this we are like a man who listens for the first time to an orchestra. He hears the chaos when the pieces begin tuning up, and then, as the concert starts, he perceives the change to a harmonious pattern of successive sounds. He cannot find the reason for this pattern by studying the separate instruments as they are played. In the movements of the conductor he thinks for a while he has the secret—a "master reaction" that determines the whole —but this does not explain the great diversity in the selections as one succeeds another. What he fails to realize is that the conductor and the players are following a course established for them by someone whom he does not see, the composer—following a work of art that organizes the performance of the various instruments into a complex harmony and sets for them a pattern and a goal. No knowledge, however great, of the physics of the instruments or the physiology of those who play them will disclose the secret of the music. This lies in the musical composition that is being performed, and in its interpretation these are but the agents.

Certainly the self-regulating, goal-seeking qualities we are here studying are qualities of *life*. At this point, and apparently only here, is the fixed crust of matter broken open, and through this gap life surges upward, opposing the downward drag to randomness and disintegration. The rest of nature is static or changes only with the ponderous slowness that formed the universe from chaos and mobilized the stars into a billion galaxies. Only life brings something *new* into this picture. With life, far more than anywhere else, we are dealing with a formative tendency, an organizing power, a spiritual force—whatever we wish to call it—that is expressed not in fixed and ancient uniformities but in the creation of something new.

What gives life this creative power is that its goals are not immutable, as the pattern of a crystal is, but are changing constantly. During the long course of evolution they altered, slowly but steadily, until new types of plants and animals came into being, adapted to every nook and corner of the earth. With the development of a nervous system came the elevation of mere bodily goals to the far more varied ones of instinct and behavior; and on man's appearance, with his capacities for memory, imagination, and rational thought, the simple goal-seeking of life at its lower levels was transformed to conscious purpose and the high aspirations of his mental and spiritual life. What so implants these goals and purposes in living stuff that in development and behavior it ever seeks to reach them and to set up still higher ones we do not know.

All this, it seems to me, makes it essential to recognize the existence of these goals of life in any system of philosophy that we may frame. Knowledge of them is essential for an understanding of life at every level, from protozoan to poet. Far more than a naïve vitalism is here involved, or a mechanism that is nothing but mechanics. Organicism sees the importance of the organized protoplasmic system but fails to take into account its purposiveness. If we were to name a point of view that recognizes both these we might call it "telism," the philosophy of goals—a belief that what is important is not the push and drive of a living system but the drawing power of a goal, conscious or unconscious, that in some way is established in it. What meaning this may have for the final problems of philosophy is not yet clear. The fact that, in the narrow segment of nature which we know, the seeking of life's goals has led already to such profound changes and promises almost limitless advances in the future suggests that purpose and creativeness may be essential qualities in the nature of the universe itself.

Life is the final problem, for only in life is the source of goal-seeking and purpose. What life's place is in the universe we have not yet discovered. It may be that which makes for order and organization in the midst of chaos. It may be the manifestation of Universal Mind operating in nature. It may be an expression of the highest possibilities latent in matter and emerging from it. In this momentous question as to the nature and quality of life we should not limit ourselves to an approach through science only, important as this is. The philosopher, the poet, the artist, and the mystic should all contribute of their insights here, for all are concerned with life. The constellation of man's deepest problems centers in biology, but in a biology broadened and illuminated by contact with our widest horizons.

CHAPTER VI

The Biology of the Spirit

Abstract

The greatest importance of the concept here presented is in its bearing on the problems of religion. If man's mind has a biological basis, his *spirit* must have one also. "Spirit" is defined as those spontaneous urgencies and desires, the basis of the emotions, which are the highest expressions of biological goal-seeking. This idea will seem inadequate to men of faith, and hopelessly mystical to materialists, but it provides a scientific interpretation for what otherwise is a nebulous concept.

In the light of this idea, some of the problems of aesthetics and religion are explored.

Values result from the fact that goals set up within us lead us to desire some things more than others. They are primarily emotional but may be much enriched by intellect.

Notable among these values is *beauty*. This is of many kinds and found at different levels. That beauty is not merely a relative quality but is rooted in life is indicated by the fact that the products of protoplasm —the physical structures of organisms—almost always appear attractive to us and often very beautiful. Beauty thus seems to be rooted in life, and we may say that whatever is in harmony with life is beautiful.

Behavior must conform to *moral values* if society is to thrive. There are various standards for right and wrong, but right, like beauty, seems not to be a merely relative quality but to be concerned with life. Behavior that furthers the attainment of an organism's normal and distinctive goals is right; that which prevents this is wrong. The penalty for wrong biological behavior is pain. Failure to attain those moral and spiritual goals which the experience of the race has found to be the highest brings more subtle forms of pain and grief. At this moral level, right is whatever helps to realize the possibilities of life most fully and wrong is what hinders this.

The goal of biological development is a single individual. Genetically each human being is different from every other. Personality, the highest form of biological organization, thus has its roots in protoplasm. This self persists through changes in substance, time, and circumstance. It is the essence of a man and the basis for the concept of the *soul*.

If the highest expression of biological goal-seeking is the human spirit, what relation can there be between this and a greater Spirit in the universe? In evolution life has reached ever higher goals and levels of organization, and has continually opposed the downward and disorganizing tendency of lifeless matter. This suggests that in nature there is a Principle of Organization which, through life, brings order out of chaos, spirit out of matter, and personality out of impersonal stuff. This principle we may identify as an attribute of God.

The conception that life is goal-seeking and that spirit is its highest expression may serve as the basis for an essentially religious personal philosophy for those who value intellectual integrity but are convinced that the universe makes sense only if interpreted in spiritual terms. Life, manifest in organisms, is integrating, purposeful, and creative. We cannot yet explain these qualities, but through them we may gain a clearer spiritual insight into man's nature and his relation to the universe than through intellect alone. If man continually seeks to elevate his goals they can lift him up to heights not dreamed of now. If he debases them he will destroy himself.

The unifying concept of man that has been presented here interprets mind and body as two aspects of the organizing, self-regulating purposiveness all living stuff displays. Around this central biological fact the great problems of philosophy, I believe, will more and more revolve. To accept the idea of man's whole nature as rooted in protoplasmic goal-seeking is to take a long step forward toward an understanding of what he is, though it is still far from "explaining" him. I cannot hope that everyone will be convinced by the evidence here presented, but the case is a substantial one and stands up sturdily, based as it is on the facts of the life sciences. It will commend itself, I believe, to all who are troubled by the old enigma of man's dual nature.

All this, though of great interest for biology, psychology, and all the other sciences of man, and of no little practical importance as well, touches but the edge of questions deeper still, the answers to which must lie finally in the domain of religious philosophy. Let us not underestimate the great importance here of the step that we propose to take. If mind can be brought back from the limbo of unreal and imaginary things and established as something that permeates not only *man*'s life but *all* life, then those other immaterial parts of him—his will, his soul, his spirit, and the rest—must also have a biological basis. Once you interpret mind in protoplasmic terms you cannot well avoid doing the same thing for these other great imponderables. This is a conclusion of the utmost moment and points at the very heart of religion, for the core of a truly religious philosophy is its concern with immaterial things, with spiritual values. If man's spirit is illusion, so must be any religion founded on spirit. If, on the other hand, there exists, in hard biological fact, a basis for the spirit like the basis we are assuming for the mind, then at least we can bring the discussion of religion into the realm of scientific respectability and recognize the life of the spirit as well as that of the mind or of the body.

The Human Spirit

It is about this concept of the spirit that the philosophy of materialism comes squarely into conflict with our western tradition. Here is the issue joined. "Spirit" is a powerful word today. In their bewilderment hosts of men, disillusioned with a world that worships matter, and losing faith in reason as the hope of safety, are seeking eagerly for this unseen thing and finding their way back to the great premise of our western culture, that the essential and eternal verities are spiritual ones. These rise above the noisy confusion of our time and stand for qualities that can offer guidance to a generation that has lost its way. "Spirit" is a word on everybody's tongue. Teachers are urged to stress *spiritual* values to their students. Our leaders exhort the nation to develop a deeper *spiritual* life. *Spirituality* is a quality to be admired. Man is a *spiritual* being, and it is in *spirit* that he must worship God.

Spirit is a dauntless thing that gropes, in a material world, for something immaterial, intangible, elusive. For many it is a lofty symbol, a quality that sets man off from matter and stands on the frontier of mystery. Others regard it not as mystery but simply unintelligible mysticism, the survival of primitive superstition that deserves no place among enlightened men. The problems that divide the world most deeply are centered not in matter but in spirit. Whether spirit is reality or illusion is the greatest question that confronts mankind. About it toss high waves of controversy. It underlies all other problems, and the answer that we give it will determine men's philosophies and the kind of world that they will build.

But here the argument is likely to drift off into a fog of hazy ideas. Just what is this thing we call the human spirit? How can we describe and deal with it? What place can it have in the pattern of our lives? How put it into words? It meant at first no more than simply "breath," and hence the breath of life. From this it came to signify the immaterial part of man that governs what he does, and thus his true and inner self, his soul, in contrast to the purely physical body where it dwells. But this immaterial part of him has many aspects that are not "spiritual." Reason is one—the intelligence to discover general principles and relate them to particular facts, thus making it possible for man to manipulate not only his environment but his ideas; the power of calling the past into the present through memory, and of picturing the possible future through imagination; the ability to divorce ideas from things and build them into patterns of abstract thought. Reason is a late arrival on the evolutionary scene. Its rudiments are found in the higher animals, but not till man appeared did this high faculty come fully to expression. Reason it was that then made possible the sudden burst of progress by which, in a few score of millennia, he far outstripped all other living things and set up his dominion in the earth.

But reason is not spirit. It is logical, cold, and fashioned finally on mathematics. This latest development of mind emerged from earlier and different psychical qualities—instincts and patterns of internally directed behavior, inborn or ready to be released by a stimulus from the outside world. A study of the lower animals shows how complex and amazing instincts are. They are the ancient and original aspects of the mind, rooted in the past and in all protoplasm, derived (so we suggest) from the primitive self-regulatory activities of the body, and grown diverse by the slow, perfective processes of evolution. Man has few instincts—perhaps only one or two—comparable to those in animals, preformed and almost automatic. In him the inner urgencies that guide behavior are no longer precisely patterned and ready to be released but are more plastic and can be directed into many courses. But inner urgencies they still remain, and they powerfully determine what he does. A human individual is no blank sheet of paper on which nothing but his environment can write, but rather a palimpsest on which appear dim tracings written there before, which easily become legible again. There come bubbling up within him a host of desires that often quite overrule his sober reason. These are experienced, subjective. Feelings and emotions are their expressions. Here is the origin of those hatreds, lusts, and passions that have disrupted human life throughout all history and do so still—our jungle heritage. But *from this same source,* let us not forget, are born man's deepest satisfactions, his cravings for beauty, his moral aspirations, his love for his fellows, and his reverence for something greater than himself in the universe outside.

These are the highest expressions, I believe, of that goal-seeking quality that begins with the formative processes in every living cell. Hence come the warmth and color of life's fabric, its richness, fullness, and diversity. Reason indeed is a powerful tool, and we do well to use it to the uttermost. The possibilities for its triumphs in the future are incalculable. But the goal of our race is not mere intellectual achievement, as some would have us think. By no discipline, however austere, can we escape the influence of those inner promptings that rise up from the living core. An existence that was rational only would be drab indeed, the plodding of a robot calculator to its uneventful end. The zest, the fire, the savor of existence comes from something deeper, something spontaneous, native, and protoplasmic, which we can never outgrow or avoid, nor should we wish to do so. These deep-seated inborn urgencies and desires, arising spontaneously in the mind but subject to a wide measure of direction, often dragging man down to the level of the beasts but coming to flower as the highest expression of what he is and what he might become, one may rightly call, I think, the human spirit.

Sharply to separate the rational from the spiritual side of man is difficult, for they grow from the same roots and are closely intermingled; but that a distinction of a sort does exist between them gains support from a knowledge of the structure and activity of the brain itself. The massive cerebral cortex, much its largest portion, is relatively recent in evolutionary origin and is well developed only in those forms where the beginnings of intelligence appear. It is very large in man and has been shown to be the seat and center of his higher mental faculties and the processes of reason. Hidden underneath its folds, however, is a far more primitive portion of the brain, the thalamus, which goes back in origin to the simplest of the vertebrate animals. Here, psychologists tell us, is the center of the instincts, of the "mental" life of man's progenitors; and here in man himself is the structure that acts as intermediary between the higher centers of the brain and that far-flung system of nerves controlling all our activities, both voluntary and involuntary ones. In the thalamus, so to speak, the whole body comes to focus. It is the seat of the emotions, the place where motives and desires are born. If the cerebral cortex is the dwelling of man's rational part, those qualities in him that we call spiritual may be said to center in the thalamus.

Granting that there is indeed one aspect of a man that may legitimately be called his spirit, if only for convenience and without implications for philosophy, one may still object that this conception is so extremely vague as hardly to be worth considering seriously. How can a scientist get at it? Spirit is still mysterious, and mystery is a quality the modern mind accepts unwillingly. It is hard to see how spirit, even if it is anchored in the brain, can ever be reduced to intelligibility. Emotions, indeed, can be studied, but not the spirit. It therefore is preposterous, many say, to speak at all of such a thing as "the biology of the spirit."

It is here that the concept of organic purposefulness developed earlier in these pages may prove serviceable. If "mind" is another name for the higher levels of what at bottom is the quality of self-regulation present in all living stuff, then these other psychical qualities, these inner urgencies, emotions, and desires that we have called the spirit, also must have biological roots. Biology deals with life, and, whatever life may be, it produces not material bodies only but poems and symphonies; the artist's imagination and the exalted visions of the seer; the heights of aspiration, self-sacrifice, and love. These may well be called fruits of the spirit, lifted above material things; but let us not forget that they are also fruits of man's physical self· and spring from the goal-seeking living stuff of which he is composed. They are a part of life, of that richer life of the emotions that distinguishes human beings from the brutes. Shakespeare was a living organism, Lincoln a protoplasmic system. Moses and Michelangelo were complex aggregations of proteins. But they were far more than these things alone. In their material substance, as in that of every great and gifted man, there somehow came to birth high qualities that the student of matter never would suspect were latent in it, qualities rising out of that deep center where life and matter and energy are inextricably mingled.

Protoplasm is a bridge between atoms, on the one hand, and the flowering of the spirit on the other. Mysteriously though man's spirit may seem to move, and high as its destiny may sometime prove to be, it is *born* in living matter, and the biologist can therefore legitimately claim it as part of his domain. Though he is a bit uncomfortable in its presence and is inclined to shift responsibility for dealing with these higher biological problems to the psychologist or the theologian, the fact remains that they *are* expressions of life and that biology can never completely understand what life in its entirety really is unless it takes them finally into account. "The great fact," says Jennings, "the striking and characteristic feature of the biologist's picture of the world, is that biological materials include sensations, emotions, desires, hopes and fears, purposes, ideas, interest, thought, imagination, knowledge. Whatever else the universe may be, it is something that brings forth these things." [1]

[1] Herbert Spencer Jennings, *The Universe and Life* (New Haven: Yale University Press, 1933) , p. 14.

The biology of the human spirit will not be easy to investigate, because experience rather than experiment is such an important part of it, and for its full development there may be required some tools that science does not now possess. It is closely entangled with the most difficult of all problems, the origin and nature of life itself. Not only orthodox biologists will be responsible for its exploration but doubtless many other students of life—the psychologist, the anthropologist, and the philosopher. The poet will have much to say about it, and the artist too. To maintain that the human spirit as here defined has qualities that cannot be explored is vastly to underrate the power of rational inquiry.

The particular advantage of the concept that has been presented here is that it brings the human spirit into more intimate association with the body instead of leaving it as something merely nebulous, intangible, and mystical. Bergson urges us to "see the life of the body just where it really is, on the road that leads to the life of the spirit. . . . The great error of the doctrines on the spirit has been the idea that by isolating the spiritual life from all the rest, by suspending it in space as high as possible above the earth, they were placing it beyond attack, as if they were not thereby simply exposing it to be taken as an effect of mirage!" [2] Just what the relation is of spirit to the body on the one hand, and to the universe on the other, is a problem we cannot solve; but to see the spirit as *born in life,* whatever its source or however lofty its final destiny may be, is a conception that helps draw it down out of the clouds and brings it closer to us.

Such an interpretation of the spirit as this will seem woefully inadequate to many. Let us admit, they will say, that

[2] Henri Bergson, *Creative Evolution,* translated by A. Mitchell (New York: Modern Library, 1911), p. 268.

the psychology of the emotions is bound to be of great importance and that it deals with human qualities that are profound in their contributions to the life and happiness of man; let us call this "spirit," if you wish, but surely this was not what Jesus meant on that memorable evening when he spoke to Nicodemus of the spirit, nor the mysterious thing to whose presence and power religion has ever borne witness. From the beginning men have felt in nature the immanence of spirit and have worshiped it. The great religions of the world have been built around it and, in Christianity, Spirit is recognized as one of the three persons in the Godhead. Men and women everywhere have drawn strength and inspiration from this reservoir. The chief evidence for the reality of spirit comes not from rational argument, anyway, but from the power it generates in human hearts, the deep conviction of its guiding presence that has changed the lives of countless men through all the centuries. And as to man himself, surely his spirit is more than the mere emotional side of his mental life, however fruitful this may be and worthy of cultivation. Man *is* a spirit, and it is as hard to fit him into a purely material mold as to weigh the beauty of a symphony on a pair of scales. Spirit interpreted by *religion* rather than by physiology and psychiatry is what men need so desperately today. Here science, whether biology or any other kind, can be of little service.

The objection thus voiced is difficult to answer without becoming deeply involved. Biology as such certainly has no jurisdiction in metaphysics or theology. There well may be no relation whatever between the human spirit as here defined and anything beyond it. Man's so-called spiritual gifts may be simply curious by-products of the physical processes of life, inextricably tied to matter and of no greater significance than the intricate markings on a shell or the petals of a lovely flower. Perhaps protoplasm secretes poems and prayers and symphonies as an oyster secretes pearls and with no greater meaning. These things would be subject matter for biology, to be sure, but of no significance at all for deeper problems. This is the familiar position of the materialist. It maintains that not only man's "spirit" but his "mind" and all similar attributes of him are only fictions and depend at last on physical events within his body, as firmly determined as the behavior of any other machine. Only this reality is final.

In such a discussion it is easy for the biologist to founder in deep and unfamiliar waters. The point I wish to make is that man, a living organism and thus legitimately within the province of the sciences of life, may be the seat of qualities that are not only worthy of our admiration and respect but may be regarded as truly spiritual in their nature. Though he has rarely taken advantage of it, the biologist is in a fortunate philosophical position, since he stands between two worlds. It is the great gap between these two—the material and the spiritual—that so long has troubled and confused mankind. If it is a *uni*verse we live in, they should somehow be related to each other. The problem today is not so much the old one of trying to "reconcile" science and religion as it is of finding how matter and spirit are associated. Living matter—protoplasm, the physical basis of life—is the point where these two meet face to face.

In some way the spinning electrons, the protons, and the score of other ultimate particles in matter are organized into atoms of carbon, hydrogen, oxygen, and nitrogen. These in turn combine to form huge molecules of protein. With various mineral elements and an abundance of water they are built into protoplasm, and then, in some way quite unknown as yet, this once dead matter suddenly comes to life.

Its material particles, no longer now at random, enter the exquisitely organized pattern of the living system. Here, and not in the origin of man, seems to be the decisive forward step, for in this simple cell lies the germ of everything life promises. Here is born not only life but all that life can be. Out of the harmonious rhythms of protoplasm come the physical processes of living things, the subject matter of biology; but from these same deep harmonies emerge as well the qualities of what we call the human spirit. Goal-seeking, creativeness, the power to mold matter to a purposed end, is present in the simplest organisms; and in man it is this same purposive and aspiring quality, I suggest, refined and elevated far above its simple origin, and revealing heights and depths unguessed in lower forms, that is the manifestation of the spirit.

The biological goals in protoplasm merge imperceptibly from bodily regulation through instinct and feeling into those aspirations that mark man at his highest. They make him a different sort of creature from a merely intellectual animal—a desiring, questing, creative being. He stands on the frontier between material and spiritual things. His spirit so transcends all else in him that it intrigues us with the hope that perhaps it even may partake of an infinite Spirit suffusing the universe itself. It reaches down into the depths of life and makes there, many are convinced, a *direct* contact with reality that seems to tell us more about our own nature and our relation to the universe than intellect alone can ever do. From it pour up into consciousness a throng of emotions and desires that are the most significant part of our experience and persuade us, mysterious though they are, that underneath the physical senses and the reasoned processes of mind there is a region full of richness, meaning, and truth but accessible only by this pathway of the spirit. Whatever name psychology may give it, and however we may try to account for what it does, we should not let a naïve materialism persuade us to neglect as useless or unreliable this spiritual avenue to reality. Many would have us believe that only through intellect can we learn the truth, that science alone can give us a clear picture of the real. When they endeavor to persuade us thus, let us remember the words of a great poet and philosopher:

> "It is not wisdom to be only wise,
> And on the inward vision close the eyes,
> But it is wisdom to believe the heart." [3]

What we are saying is that the human spirit is not mere meaningless emotion, without significance, but that it has a characteristic quality of its own and moves toward its own goals, blocked and fettered though it often is by circumstance. Protoplasm, in which it comes to birth, also has a characteristic quality and is no random, indeterminate thing. One of the important generalizations of biology is that everywhere, from amoeba to man, protoplasm is very much the same. Life is unique. It is not based on a wide variety of physical systems, diverse in quality and structure, but on a very precise sort of stuff. This is the basis for a belief that life and the spirit that grows out of it may be expected to display particular predispositions of their own.

But psychology seeks for the origin of man's attitudes, motives, and emotional life not in any specific quality of his protoplasm but chiefly in his early conditioning, his cultural influences and education. It takes no cognizance of anything as mysterious as a human "spirit." Even if the psychologist were to admit the existence and importance of goal-seeking, he would still look to conditioning to explain

---

[3] George Santayana, "O world, thou choosest not the better part!"

what goals are actually sought, and not to any protoplasmic preferences.

Here is the issue joined between those who see in man no more than a physical mechanism, however marvelous, and those who are convinced that through this spiritual part of him there is to be heard at least a whisper of a reality beyond the world of time and space and matter that so engages us on every hand. Which side each of us will take is governed more by inner conviction than by argument, but the decision is momentous, for whether religion has real meaning or is but wishful thinking depends on what we believe about the spirit of man. If all the goal-seeking, desiring, and aspiring of our spirits are but curious tensions in a protoplasmic mechanism, they are still of interest and importance in many ways; but if, beyond all this, they provide a means of communion with something in the universe that can be apprehended in no other way, then does their significance indeed transcend all other human qualities.

Here, I think, is the essential meaning of what is called by the venerable name of "faith." As man emerged into intelligence he was beset by a host of problems, both in nature and within himself, which pressed him to be answered. Through the centuries some of the simpler ones he has been able to solve by the power of science and in other ways; but there are many, and among them the most vital ones of all, which do not yield to intellectual attack. Among the many answers that are offered to them he must stake his life on those which seem to him the most convincing and most satisfying. His spiritual insights are of vital service here. From them arise those inner convictions and assurances that help him find his way. To be sure, these do not yield the comforting certainties that logical reason offers, but in that wide sea of the unknown they offer the only compass that he has.

Faith in *something* is a vital necessity, and in the direct contact with reality itself which man makes through the avenue of his spirit, he finds the surest foundation for a faith. Differ though men may in their interpretation of what this inner voice reveals, it still remains the only monitor when reason can go no further. Faith is a venture of the spirit.

If we are willing to accept this idea that man's spirit is the highest expression of what began as the formative, self-regulating quality found in all living stuff, we shall discover that it leads to the center of some of the great problems of aesthetics and religion—values, beauty, morality, the soul, and the idea of God. It will be worth our while, I think, to look at each of these from the point of view of biological purposiveness, from the concept that an inherent and essential character of all life is goal-seeking.

Values

The act of self-regulation, of purposiveness, implies the presence of something to regulate *to,* a goal that is being sought. The reactions of a living thing to its environment are such as will help it reach this goal. It seeks conditions of light or temperature or situation that are favorable to the attainment and the maintenance of its particular inner organization. The young plant bends toward the light. The trout seeks a cool and flowing stream. Living things react *toward* something.

In what it takes into its body, also, every organism is selective. Among the objects around it there are some which, at the purely biological level, it seems to "prefer" over others. The humble amoeba thrusts out its strands of protoplasm toward certain substances and draws these into itself, but pulls back from others. Thus it regulates its bodily economy. A higher animal seeks the particular kinds of food by which its goals of physiological satisfaction can be gained. Every cell of a plant or animal, through the quality of its surrounding membranes, permits certain substances to enter it and excludes others, and by this simple sort of preference maintains its precisely organized inner equilibrium. The significance of these various choices is that they are made with reference to a particular state, which at the time is the organism's biological goal. Indeed, when a cell or an organism ceases its selective behavior toward the outside world, and allows everything to enter it or leave it, we know that it is dead.

At the primitive psychical level—if our theory is correct —this goal is inwardly felt as something *desired,* at first unconsciously and instinctively, but with greater vividness in higher forms, and especially in man. The beginnings of desire, of the feelings of wanting or seeking, thus are rooted in a quest for whatever will help attain a particular end. Desires are not capricious preferences but evidences of goals set up within us that draw us toward them. The presence of these goals is also the basis of other powerful emotions— of hope, anticipation, regret, and despair. These lose their meaning unless interpreted in terms of something wished for.

Man has many bodily goals that clamor for fulfillment and thus generate a host of desires—for food, for shelter, for mates. These are sought instinctively, and primitive man doubtless gave little rational thought to what they were. He simply *wanted* them. They were not necessarily the things that were good for him, but through the long selective processes of evolution individuals who preferred harmful goals were weeded out. Such preferences long helped to regulate his activities, maintain his life, and perpetuate his species. These same inborn preferences guide much of what men eagerly seek today.

Above these physical urgencies are other things man desires—achievement, self-expression, power, and much else. Such things minister not to his bodily life but to the life of his mind and help him reach those inner goals that are so powerful in determining what he does. Men differ greatly in the things they want, but for no one is the world a monochrome, a flat and monotonous series of impressions and events. By virtue of our inner preferences each of us recognizes features in it that stand out through their attractiveness, and others that repel us.

Man, the goal-seeking animal, is sensitive to still higher things than these, and at his best he longs for them—abstract, imponderable qualities like beauty, goodness, love, and truth. The universal testimony of the race approves them as our highest goals. Though often led astray by desires for something lower, man comes back always to these qualities as supremely worthy of his seeking. In his inmost heart he craves them.

All these things that we prefer and seek, from purely bodily satisfactions to the highest spiritual goals, become our values. One of the most difficult things to understand about a man is why he values some things over others. This is the very key to his nature, unlocking to us what he really is. To relate values at all levels to the basic goal-seeking that is an essential feature of all life helps us to see them against the background of man in his entirety—not as something random and meaningless, but as an index of his deepest qualities, rooted in his very living fabric. To show that values have a biological basis does not explain them fully, but at least it points to the source from which they grow.

One notable fact about values is that they belong prima-

rily to the emotional and not the intellectual side of man.
The simplest are expressions of mere physical desire. Higher
ones come from more refined preferences, and the highest
of all are part of man's spiritual life. Values are centered
more in the thalamus than in the cortex. To be sure, they
may be greatly changed and elevated, and one of the chief
tasks of education is to do this. Values can be enriched
by reason and guided into logical paths, and it is fortunate
that this is so; but in their primitive freshness and vigor
they spring from a level deeper than the intellect. Even rational values, like those a scientist seeks, in many cases have
a basis that is essentially emotional rather than intellectual.
In their highest flowering, values are evidence of those vital
urgencies that we have called the human spirit. They tell us
something important about life itself. They are guideposts
we should follow to find the direction in which life is moving.

Two objections may be raised to the conclusion that values are important in telling us anything about life as such,
or that they have any deep philosophical significance. First,
it is argued that the things we value are those that have
become embedded in us, so to speak, by natural selection
during the course of evolution. We value what it is good for
us to value—food, offspring, survival itself. A species by
which these things were not eagerly sought would soon
cease to cumber the earth. The reproductive instinct, cul-
minating in mother love, is thus interpreted as the basis
of altruism, for instinctive antisocial and immoral values
would certainly handicap their possessors and the societies
in which they appeared. Second, and from quite a different
direction, it may be objected that values, save perhaps as
related to a few basic instincts, are not fixed in us at all but
result from the environment in which we grow. What we

like depends on what we are brought up to like. Education and conditioning determine this, just as they do behavior in general. The preferences of Italians for spaghetti and of Americans for ice-cream soda are not born in them. All children are hungry, to be sure, but what they like to eat is largely determined by how they are brought up. Other tastes are largely environmental too. The music that pleases a Chinese is something quite different from a Beethoven symphony; but such preferences are acquired, not inherited. Moral values also are acquired. Those of the Andaman Islanders are very different from our own, but this is the result of geography and history.

To explain these powerful affinities as psychological drives derived at last from their usefulness in survival among our ancestors, or to regard them simply as the strange vagaries of a biochemical machine, implanted in it by its environment, seems difficult indeed. We can hardly avoid the conviction that they have a more profound meaning. If men are robots, pushed about by every wind of fate, why do they show such consistent preferences for immaterial things like beauty and goodness? This problem of values long has puzzled philosophers and still disturbs the complacency of materialism. Whatever the final explanation of all this may be, one thing, I think, can be maintained: We value those qualities that are in harmony with something inside us, with one or another of those biological norms or goals to which we here have been attributing all motivation, all purposive action, and which have their roots in the very fabric of our living stuff.

We can understand them better, perhaps, if we consider more fully the biological basis for some of man's chief values.

Beauty

What is beauty, that we so should value it? What selective advantage, in a competition for survival, can there be in any love for it? In man's long upward struggle the pursuit of beauty has sometimes actually been a handicap, for uncouth barbarians too often were victorious over men of higher cultivation and aesthetic sensibilities. Our love for beauty is hard to attribute to the tough give-and-take of evolutionary selection. It is a peculiarly human quality. Beasts possess only the rudiments of it. Indeed, it was when our primitive ancestor first undertook to decorate his body and the products of his hands with patterns which to him seemed beautiful that he finally could be said to have become a man.

Beauty appeals to something deep within us. Our love of it *feels* like something native to our hearts, indigenous there, and not acquired just for its usefulness. "Beauty is its own excuse for being." What does it mean that we should be so deeply moved by the harmonies of a Beethoven symphony or a majestic chorus, or by a simple song of Stephen Foster? Why do we throng to see the glories of Rembrandt at the National Gallery? Whence comes the ecstasy that fills us as we behold the sun setting in glory or the panorama of a snow-clad mountain range spread out before us? Why does the soaring beauty of Mont-Saint-Michel so lift us up? Why, generation after generation, do men return to Shakespeare and to Milton or listen to more ancient melodies in "the surge and thunder of the Odyssey"? What is there in all these to commend them to our hearts, save their inherent loveliness? We are hungry for this food of the spirit as we are for bodily nourishment. The feeling for beauty cannot be described or measured. It can only be *felt*, but it has its own inner warrant and authority. "There is a side of our personality," says Eddington, "which impels us to dwell on beauty and other aesthetic significancies in Nature, and in the work of man, so that our environment means to us much that is not warranted by anything found in the scientific inventory of its structure. An overwhelming feeling tells us that this is right and indispensable to the purpose of our existence. . . . We do not defend the validity of seeing beauty in a natural landscape. We accept with gratitude the fact that we are endowed to see it that way." [4]

One may object that beauty cannot be of very great significance since there are no absolute standards by which to judge it, and since our own opinions of it change with time and circumstance. What Victorian taste admired we often now abhor and doubtless our own descendants will smile at the things we like today. Fashions in beauty, as in women's clothes, change constantly, and even connoisseurs may violently disagree. Still greater are the differences imposed by culture and geography, for what the Orient and Africa regard as lovely are often quite unsuited to our western tastes. How can beauty be anything but a temporary fancy, one may ask, when even the same person may come to change his opinion as to what it is?

Let us freely admit that beauty, like truth, is of many kinds and to be sought in many different places. Conformity here is hopeless to expect, nor should we seek to impose it. The sort of beauty that speaks to our hearts will depend in part on actual differences in what we can see and hear, on the inborn quality of our sense organs. Some men can never

[4] Arthur S. Eddington, *The Nature of the Physical World* (Cambridge: Cambridge University Press, 1929) , p. 107.

learn to appreciate music, and others are but little moved by works of art. More often, what we look upon as beautiful results from our surroundings and our bringing up, from what we have *learned* to like. This liking can be cultivated. For one who naturally responds to music, be-bop usually loses its attractiveness if he listens well to Beethoven. Acquaintance with the classics in literature is the best way to cure a taste for the comics. Men who learn to know the great painters are no longer satisfied with mere calendar art. Tastes in any field can be elevated by cultivation and by keeping good aesthetic company, and for this we should indeed be thankful. Though it may fl tuate from person to person, year to year, and continent to continent, the aesthetic judgment of mankind tends slowly to sort beauty out from ugliness and the more beautiful from the less. Whatever its nature, *beauty* is the treasure that we value—a pattern of qualities in harmony with our spirits, something that vibrates on the same wave length as the living stuff of which we are composed.

These cravings for the beautiful, rising from the deep inner core of life, are evidence, it seems to me, that something in nature exists by which they can be satisfied, just as hunger shows that there is such a thing as food. The argument that beauty is transient or meaningless holds no persuasion for one whose spirit has once felt the enravishment of loveliness. Beauty is *real*, and we can seek it out. "In the appreciation of music and of pictures," says C. E. M. Joad, "we get a momentary and fleeting glimpse of the nature of that reality to a full knowledge of which the movement of life is progressing. . . . We are, if I may so put it, for the moment *there*, just as a traveler may obtain a fleeting glimpse of a distant country from a height passed on the way, and cease for a space from his journey to enjoy the view." [5] Said Santayana, who was sensitive to aesthetic values as few men have been, "Beauty is a pledge of the visible conformity between the soul and nature and consequently a ground for faith in the supremacy of the good." [6]

Such exalted expressions of biological goal-seeking as are these cravings for beauty tell us something reassuring about ourselves and about the universe: about ourselves, that innate in the living stuff that forms us there are goals of the spirit worthy to command our allegiance; and about the universe, that it is a place where such goals can hopefully be sought.

For one who regards this plea for the reality and significance of beauty as too nebulous and mystical for a tough mind, let us go back to the foundation of our argument, to the organizing, purposive, creative quality in all of life, for it is a remarkable fact that we find beauty at the very heart of life itself. A plant or animal draws into itself diffuse and random matter from the world outside and builds it into the organized living pattern of its body. Here, in a way that passes our understanding, it becomes endowed with that self-regulating and purposive quality this book has so often discussed. But equally remarkable, I think, is the fact that these organic structures, these material husks that living stuff has built to house itself, are of such character and quality that almost invariably man has regarded them as beautiful. Some of the loveliest things we know are made by this unconscious artistry of life. The lilies of the field excel the glories of King Solomon, and flowers, like nothing else on earth, refresh the spirit of man. What created things are lovelier than birds—unless it be butterflies! Sea shells in

[5] *Philosophical Aspects of Modern Science* (New York: The Macmillan Company, 1943), p. 310.
[6] George Santayana, *The Sense of Beauty* (New York: Charles Scribners Sons, 1936).

their myriad shapes and hues are a joy to gather. Trees lift up the eyes and the heart. Wherever one turns he is confronted with this beauty of the form and color of life. To leaf through the pages of such a volume as Haeckel's magnificent *Kunstformen der Natur* is to be overwhelmed by the variety and richness of organic patterns.

Such beauty varies in degree, to be sure, from masterpieces of morphogenesis to less attractive forms, but almost never does nature let us down or fail to make a pleasing pattern. Not only at the level of what is easily seen is beauty evident, for the microscope reveals such an exquisite delicacy of texture everywhere, from the pattern of a diatom shell to the stellate hair upon the surface of a leaf, that we are amazed at the protoplasmic craftsmanship that has created them. Surely beauty of this sort came not from competition or selective advantage, nor does it change with time and circumstance. The tendency to create it is a quality of life, implanted in all protoplasm. We may say, I think, that life expresses itself in beauty as it does in metabolism or in self-regulation or in any other biological character.

It is no wonder, therefore, that we admire this living beauty, for it is native to us. We are drawn from that same protoplasmic lineage that produces it. But it is significant, I think, that we respond to the beauties of inorganic nature also—of stars and snowflakes and precious stones, of sunsets, rainbows, mountains, and the sea. Beauty is no mere biological by-product. It is everywhere. Living stuff not only creates it but has at last produced, in man, a being who, by his spiritual sensitivity, can reach out and discover beauty in far wider realms and can begin to create new and undiscovered forms of it.

Here is art's great service to the human spirit. The painter, the musician, and the poet bring to its highest expression that same organizing and creative quality the germ of which all life possesses. Just as an organism takes random matter and builds it into a living bodily pattern, so the man of art takes meaningless canvas, paint, and marble, musical sounds and the more subtle symbols of written and spoken words, and builds them into patterns that catch up a bit of the beauty of nature and interpret it to our spirits. He uses these symbols as a means of communicating his vision of beauty when it cannot be grasped by the intellect but must speak to something deeper in us. The artist's task is to serve thus as intermediary between man and nature by expressing the inborn longing of man's spirit for order and beauty, which is rooted in the very quality of his life, in terms that bring it into harmony with the wider orderliness and beauty in the universe outside.

Moral Values

In living organisms there are not only goals that express themselves in the form and patterned structure of the body —and which may be said to reach their highest expression in a work of art—but goals to which the *behavior* of the organism conforms. Structure and behavior are both expressions of protoplasmic activity, and thus not sharply distinguishable from each other; but behavior is concerned primarily with the functions of the body rather than with its physical form. The simplest of activities are physiological processes. We have seen that an organism tends to maintain a constant inner state, which is restored if altered—in body temperature, blood sugar concentration, and many other things. More obvious activities are bodily movements. In most animals these are under the control of the nervous system and in the lower forms are governed by instincts, simple psychological expressions of protoplasmic regulation. In man, with his highly developed brain and his wide range of goals that often are in conflict, behavior has become very complex. Most acts are now determined by conscious choice rather than by instinct. In an earlier chapter the biological basis for the motivation of conduct was discussed, and the importance of wanting the *right* things was emphasized. This idea of a "right" and a "wrong" in behavior results from those human relationships that grow out of man's life in social groups. Hence have arisen the moral codes by which he has sought to live with his neighbors in peace and justice.

One of man's chief problems is to determine what the basis of a moral code should be, to find out what he *ought* to do. Is the right that which is the word of God given to man in the Ten Commandments? Is it what is revealed to us by conscience and intuition? Is it whatever will increase the sum of human happiness? Is it that which is the most reasonable thing to do? Is it whatever makes for the fullness and perfection of life? Above all, is there any absolute right, anything embedded, so to speak, in the nature of the universe, which should guide our actions? Or are right and wrong simply relative, dependent on time and place and culture pattern, and changing with environment and circumstance? What, in short, is the basis of our moral values? These questions are of vital importance in a day when intellectual power threatens to outrun moral control and thus destroy us.

Similar questions, you remember, are asked about aesthetic values, and these can be answered in much the same way. It may well be argued that moral values are the result of competition and selection, since no society can well survive which does not condemn and strive to stamp out lying, theft, and murder. We are familiar, too, with the wide changes moral codes have undergone with time and place. The puritanism of seventeenth-century England gave place to eighteenth-century laxity and this, in turn, to the rigid codes of the nineteenth century. These now have yielded to something different still. The moral standards east of Suez, too, are often different from our own.

The reasons for these differences are easy to understand, and yet for many the conviction sturdily persists that man *does* have an inborn love for virtue; that there *are* moral values to which behavior persistently returns; that the human spirit has its natural instincts and cravings as the body does. "Conscience" is still a powerful word, despite the assurance of psychology that it is simply the result of conditioning, of what we learn to value. The good, like the beautiful, has many sides, and no one can hope to comprehend it all or to gather it into any simple code; but just as there is an inner sensitivity to beauty in its many forms, so I believe there is an inner sensitivity, rooted in life itself, that recognizes and values for themselves such qualities as honesty, justice, courage, unselfishness, and other things men commonly regard as virtuous. As life comes to high expression in beauty, so we may say it also does in righteousness and love. Though much of what is right can be apprehended by the intellect—just as much of beauty can be—the final recognition of its value is an act of the human spirit.

Thus to claim that we can be helped to determine what is right by an inner sensitivity or conscience will doubtless leave many unconvinced, as it always has. There is, however, a sound biological argument that differences do exist between right and wrong that are not merely relative and temporary but inherent in the nature of life itself. It is provided in the concept which is here our central theme—that motive and purpose, and thus all behavior, grow out of the goal-seeking character of living things.

In even the simplest forms of life there is a physiological norm or "steady state," which tends to maintain itself. So long as it is undisturbed the organism flourishes and presumably experiences whatever is the simplest forerunner of ease or gratification. Higher up the scale, where bodily goals have become consciously desired, their fulfillment leads to feelings of contentment and of pleasure. The satisfaction of still higher goals brings keener happiness, and if our spiritual longings are fulfilled such ecstasy may follow as to be beyond the power of any words. For goal-achievement at every level there are appropriate rewards of inner satisfaction.

Many factors, however, may disturb this delicate organic equilibrium. It may be upset by injury, disease, the attack of enemies, changing environment, and many other things. In the higher animals, at least, the signal that the balance is upset, the norm diverted, is not mere cessation of pleasure. It is pain. Where the nervous system is much simpler than our own, pain presumably is felt much less—at least fishermen and hunters ought to hope that this is so!—but it seems probable that some unease, some vague prototype of pain, some "tension," must be common to the whole organic world. It is a signal that all is not well.

Bodily pain in man has the same source. Pain from a burned finger, the sting of a wasp, too many green apples, or an inflamed appendix, are indications of danger to our bodily economy, signs that the nicely balanced organic system is out of order somewhere. Often the corrective comes by almost automatic regulation. More commonly, in the higher types of life, the organism has to learn by experience what actions are injurious and must be avoided under

penalty of pain. Without pain's warning we should run past
the danger signals until it was too late to restore the threatened balance of life. Pain is therefore not mere meaningless
suffering. There is a reason for it. It has importance for survival. Sensitivity to threatened ill is an advantage in the
struggle for existence. The more susceptible an animal is to
pain, the more complex will be the life it can sustain. Evolutionary advance has been bought with a price, and part of
this price is a greater sensitivity to, an increased awareness
of, both pain and pleasure.

To account for pain as retribution for Adam's sin, as mor-
alists have been wont to do, is therefore to take far too narrow a view of this deep question. In such a concept animals
certainly should never suffer pain, as higher ones seem
obviously to do. Nevertheless, it is clear that pain, whether
physical or mental, has important moral implications. When
an animal does something that disturbs its norm, the bodily
goal set up within it, it does "wrong," it commits the prototype of what in man is called by the unpopular name of
"sin." For this the punishment is pain, which seems to be at
bottom the penalty for any disturbance of a biological system. In lower animals regulatory action almost automatically restores the balance, but in higher forms, and especially in man, such regulation is not automatic, and to
restore the norm requires a conscious directive from the
brain. As free agents we by no means always choose to heed
pain's signal, and thus we are responsible for what we may
suffer as a consequence. If there were no such things as freedom and conscious choice, why should pain be necessary?
An automaton could regulate its behavior readily enough,
and for an automaton to have to suffer seems a ghastly
thing. The question of pain goes deeper than this biological
explanation, however, and in the undeserved suffering of

innocence it raises moral and religious problems of the utmost gravity. All we can say here, perhaps, is that pain, wherever it appears, is a sign that something, somewhere, has gone wrong.

To rid ourselves of pain, discomfort, or unhappiness, experienced in the present or foreseen as coming sometime in the future, is therefore an important goal of life, negative though it be. It often conflicts with goals that are pleasurable temporarily. A cup of coffee at dinner may be paid for by a sleepless night. Discarding an overcoat on a mild winter day may cause a cold. Such, if you will, are simple physiological "sins"—the pursuit of goals that are attractive but in their attainment conflict with more deeply seated and elemental ones, and thus exact inexorable retribution because they run counter to some fundamental biological norm. They are the forerunners of more serious violations, at a higher level, of other laws of life.

But there are goals that govern our behavior which are far more complex than these physiological ones—longings, ambitions, purposes; all of them manifestations, we may assume, of this same goal-seeking character of living stuff. Among them may be named all things that men desire—noble and base and the whole spectrum in between. The anguish that comes when they are unfulfilled is often more poignant than mere physical pain. Hopes deferred, ambitions unattained, and aspirations finally denied, all end in bitterness of spirit. Many never *can* be realized because of incompatibilities among them. Between these various goals unfortunate man is pulled this way and that. He has to choose which ones to seek and which ones to ignore. Often he finds that though to gain one end is pleasurable, it finally prevents achievement of another more important one and thus results at last in sorrow and remorse. Happiness, satisfaction, the sense of virtue and of high accomplishment —these all men at their best will eagerly pursue; but lower goals prevent the accomplishment of higher ones. God's ends and Mammon's cannot both be gained.

In the very nature of life, so it would seem—and has been proved by the experience of the race—the achievement of some goals brings misery, frustration, or disaster, and not happiness. To violate the welfare of another person, as by lying to him, stealing from him, or taking away his life, is completely to prevent the attainment of those highest satisfactions which experience has shown can come only if we have affection for our fellow men and treat them as we would ourselves be treated. To "sin," it seems to me, is not simply to do a particular thing that is called wrong but—deeper than this—to seek an end which, if reached, will betray the seeker, for it will prevent attainment of the only goals that finally will satisfy him. The moral life consists of *wanting* the right goals so much that lesser ones no longer are attractive. Character is the constant habit not simply of doing right deeds but of desiring right ends.

To aid us in distinguishing right from wrong we therefore have, it seems to me, a criterion with a sound biological basis. In the simplest cases, that act is "right" which helps maintain the normal and essential goals of life and thus leads to feelings of satisfaction and pleasure; "wrong" is whatever tends to prevent the attainment of these goals. It can be recognized by the fact that it results in physical or mental pain. Since there are different levels in our goals —from physical well-being to wider gratifications and finally to the loftiest aspirations of the spirit—the moral level of our conduct will depend on the goal with which it is concerned. Overeating is a physiological "sin" but surely not as debasing as to tell a lie or deliberately to seek bodily pleasure at the expense of higher satisfactions. In the complex clash of goals, a painful effect is often hard to trace to a particular violation, but at least the biological basis for an ethical code is here at hand.

This concept, in its simplest terms, regards as right *whatever helps to realize the possibilities of life most fully*. The moral imperative, the "ought," is thus related to a norm inherent in protoplasm itself. Right thus has much the same status that beauty does. Both are vast and many-sided. Both are difficult to grasp in their entirety. Both in a sense are absolutes, since they are in harmony with something fundamental, the nature of life itself.

The universe seems to possess a "structure," and our judgments of aesthetic and moral values result from the degree of spiritual sensitivity our living systems have to what this structure is. These judgments are not fixed and certain. They may swing back and forth and tempt us to believe that they are vagrant and erratic things; but, like the needle of a compass, they slowly come to rest and point the direction in which nature moves. They are not weathervanes but guideposts. Whatever eternal values there may be, and whatever absolute truth, it is through these spiritual sensitivities, reinforced by our faculty of rational judgment, that we can discover them. As a blind-flying airplane is sensitive to the beam that guides it and thus finds its way through what would otherwise be trackless space, so are these inner monitors sensitive to the structure of the universe through which we journey, and we can safely follow them to our final destination. Though we may fail miserably in attaining these high values, the fact that we know they are high should give us courage. With Rabbi Ben Ezra we can say

> What I aspired to be,
> And was not, comforts me.

In these perilous and troubled days the problem of moral values is tied so closely to the success of our complex and worldwide social order that it assumes an importance even greater than it had in earlier and more parochial times. What, we may ask, is the chief value that should govern man's relations with his fellows, not only his immediate neighbors but those of other races, nations, and beliefs? Is it selfishness, which slips so easily into hatred and a desire to injure and destroy? Or is it love, that benign affection in which concern for self expands to solicitude for others? Which "helps to realize the possibilities of life most fully"?

Here is the center of the battle, the nucleus around which other moral problems all converge. Here too is the test of how dependable our intuitive spiritual judgments are in moral issues. Surely in primitive man and his prehuman ancestors inborn and instinctive attitudes—precursors of spiritual ones—must have been such as to foster the survival of the individual and thus have been inherently selfish ones. A few, concerned with care of young and with collective behavior in social organisms, contained the germs of altruism; but man's "animal nature" still was centered primarily in the welfare of himself or his immediate group. Only as he came to be truly human, and especially as he drew together into societies, did this instinctively selfish attitude begin to change. It still is powerful and the source of endless cruelty and hate, as the world well knows today, and we must sorrowfully admit that in the refinement of his cruelty man far excels all other animals; but competing with this jungle heritage, as man rose from barbarism, has emerged a growing reverence for quite different attitudes—for love, unselfishness, and altruism. In their hearts—often in contrast to their actual behavior—most men recognize these as supreme spiritual values. The rejection of them by the ideology of communism is what offers such a serious threat to us today. Despite this barbarous lapse we must admit, I think, that love has a mandate in the hearts of men whose spiritual aspirations have risen above the level of the beasts'. Love is the climax of all goal-seeking, protoplasm's final consummation. To love your neighbor as yourself is the only basis for human relationships. "Love," says Sorokin, "is the supreme value around which all moral values can be integrated into one ethical system valid for the whole of humanity." [7] Unless we set this value up as our high spiritual goal, we may lose all the treasures that mankind has gained. Only through love can the Kingdom of Heaven at last be won.

The Soul

Our values tell us much about what we are and what life is, but they do not touch a far more pressing and personal matter, the problem of the soul. What can be said for that imponderable, precious thing? Can any basis be discovered for it, any hope for its existence and reality? In a universe that seems so convincingly material and impersonal, is there any evidence that individual and immaterial personalities have significance at all? Great thinkers have long discussed this question, but have come to no agreement. Is there any contribution to it, we may ask, which can come from the idea of organic purpose that has been developed here? I believe there is.

The tendency of all life to goal-seeking, its regulation toward norms, leads inevitably to the production of *a single*

---

[7] Pitirim A. Sorokin, *The Ways and Power of Love* (Boston: The Beacon Press, 1954), p. 486.

whole individual, a living organism. "The living body," says Bergson, "has been separated and closed off by nature herself. It is composed of unlike parts that complete each other. It performs diverse functions that involve each other. It is an *individual,* and of no other object, not even of a crystal, can this be said, for a crystal has neither difference of parts nor diversity of functions." [8]

When the individual is disturbed in structure or activity, it tends to restore itself. In the simplest organisms, as we have seen, if the body is cut into pieces each piece will restore the parts that are missing to regenerate a complete and perfect whole. In higher types, and especially when they are in their mature state, this power is much weakened; but a piece of living stuff, until it becomes too tightly bound by immutable matter, tends, if isolated, to remake an individual. The remarkable fact is that this does not happen if the parts are in contact and communication with one another, for then each part assumes its proper structure, function, and position in the whole. Only if the pieces are separated, either physically or by the breakdown of communication between them, does each proceed to develop by itself. By one means or another an individual, not an indeterminate mass of living stuff, comes into being.

An individual organism can be defined as a dynamic system of goals, a bundle of biological purposes. The psychological aspect of this is the *self.* Psychology is concerned with the *whole* person. Unlike medicine and physiology, which have generally dealt with particular parts or processes, the science of the mind is interested in the unified individual, and especially in this individual as a self-regulating system, homeostatic in the broadest sense. A recent text defines the

[8] Henri Bergson, loc. cit., p. 12.

self as "an elaborate pattern of desired constant states, which are protected if anything threatens them." [9]

This self, this psychological pattern of goals, developing from the simpler biological pattern of the self-regulating organism, is the basis of human personality. It is a most remarkable thing. "It maintains its integrity in space and time. It persists. It has a history. However long its history may be, however varied its surroundings and its activities, it remains the same individual. Matter enters and leaves it, and its material constitution may be replaced many times, but its fundamental organization is unaltered. It is unique; not just one of a long series of similar units, but unlike—or so it seems—any other individual that ever lived. An unchanging genetic constitution is doubtless of basic importance here, but characteristics acquired during the individual's history— bodily skills, memories, tastes, and prejudices—are also built into the persisting self. For any living machine to maintain the delicate physiological balance necessary for life is remarkable enough, but to preserve its specific character as well, unaltered by the flux of chemical and physical change, is indeed past understanding now. Human personality, tenuous as it may sometimes seem to be, is of surprisingly tough fiber. The knot of norms, goals, steady states, potencies, and purposes of which it is composed is almost impossible to loosen. To kill it is easy, and to direct the course of its development not difficult; but to break it down and make it into something different as a sculptor does with his clay; to shake it free from its past, to destroy its identity—this the organized pattern of personality most successfully resists." [10]

[9] Ross Stagner and T. F. Karwoski, *Psychology* (New York: McGraw-Hill Company, 1952) , p. 18.

[10] Edmund W. Sinnott, *Two Roads to Truth* (New York: The Viking Press, 1953) , p. 126.

How this feat is accomplished we do not know, but the persistence of the individual in biology and of the self in man is a major fact of life.

Each of us is a separate center of vital activity, a unique bundle of goals that are our very own and differ from those sought by any other living thing. This self is precious to us. *Self*ishness is bound to be implanted in every human being. It is the expression of a fundamental biological quality, essential if life is to continue. But individuals must live together, and society therefore makes its own demands as well. In the great human drama Self and Society play the leading roles, and the plot is that ancient conflict between the innate self-seeking of the biological individual and the unselfish attitudes that are necessary if men are to form that greater organism with higher goals, the good society.

In all this it should never be forgotten—as some are wont to do—that each self is unique. Men could be so much more easily manipulated if this were not so! Genetics understands today far better than did Darwin the nature of that biological variability we all display. It seems certain that no two individuals on earth today (identical twins excepted) are exactly alike in their inborn qualities or like any other individual who has ever lived. Each self is not only a single knot of purposes and predilections but has its own particular and private character. Each man, woman, and child is not a unit or a statistic only, but a *person*. In any plans that we may have for man, this unique individuality of every member of his race must never be disregarded. Dollars are all alike, and miles and pounds, and can be freely interchanged, but not men. There is no Bureau of Standards to make them uniform, and let us hope there never will be.

This individual self, this personality centered in living stuff, persistent amid the flux of time and circumstance, aware of itself and of the universe around it, able through memory to look back and through imagination to foresee and mold the future—it is this self, the essence of a man, that offers a foundation for the concept of the soul. By many the soul is looked on as a mere superstition and without importance, one of the myths that man in his enlightenment should now discard. And yet this persistent tendency of life to round itself up into unique individuals from which the fine flower of human personality has come indicates that these may be more permanent and significant than ephemeral pieces of protoplasmic machinery; that they may have meaning in the universe; that they may even be worth "saving"!

The concept developed in these pages suggests a further possibility about the soul. Materialism regards the body as dominant and thinks of the immaterial part of man as riding along upon it, so to speak—an epiphenomenon, like the picture on a television screen. But if body and mind have a common source, how can we tell which dominates the other? On such a view it is just as logical to look on the mind—or the soul—as the essential member of the pair. Perhaps the material part of man is the *product* of the soul! It was Charles Kingsley, I believe, who suggested that the soul secretes the body as a snail its shell. Edmund Spenser said this more poetically:

> For of the soule the bodie form doth take:
> For soule is forme, and doth the bodie make.

At least in the sort of monism we have been advocating, matter is not master. If in the universe there is an organizing principle, it may be that some of it dwells in each of us as his own soul—not a transient and temporary configuration in atoms and molecules and quanta, but part of an eternal, universal Spirit. The soul is the highest level of that goal-seeking, integrating process that is life. It is a magnificent hypothesis, and, as any good hypothesis should do, it accounts for many facts that otherwise would be quite meaningless. Until we know far more about the unsolved problems that cluster around every living thing, we should not be too hasty in denying the possibility of its existence.

God

But there is a deeper problem here than all these. Granted that man has a spirit, the highest and finest expression of the possibilities that lie hidden in dead matter and waiting to be called forth by life; granted that this spirit can develop an exquisite sensitivity to beauty, truth, and goodness; granted that it is worthy of our admiration and respect, and that around it can be built, as humanism tries to do, a faith in man and a reverence for what he may become that even ministers to many as a religion; granted all this, what relation can there be between this spirit and a greater one in the universe outside? Religion makes the adventurous leap from the spirit of man to the Universal Spirit it calls God. The power of religion, the assurance and the consolation that it brings, depend on the belief that the essential reality in nature is spirit.

To this great question as to the existence and attributes of God, the most profound that man can ask, one hardly expects our slender hypothesis to contribute anything very new or useful. Against the background of this idea of goal-seeking as the essence of life, however, it may be possible to look at the problems even of theology in a somewhat different light. Why living stuff should be so organized that norms or goals are set up in it to which its activities conform is still a biological enigma. In an earlier chapter we have seen the difficulties of explaining this in terms of present scientific concepts, and have discussed the suggestions of various thinkers that there is in nature an organizing power, a "wholeness tendency" as yet not understood, which pulls matter together into systems, of which living organisms are perhaps not the only examples. Such an idea has much to commend it. Attention has often been called to the curious contrast between organic evolution and the Second Law of Thermodynamics. Through evolution has come a succession of living things that shows progressively higher levels of organization. The organic world has constantly moved upward. The Second Law, on the other hand, expresses the undoubted fact that lifeless matter tends to *decrease* in the degree of its organization, to grow more and more random in character, that the universe tends to "run down." As the physicist puts it, entropy increases. There seem to be in nature these two opposing streams—the tendency toward organization and goal-seeking, and the tendency toward chance and randomness. The upward, purposeful thrust of life, which continually opposes the downward drag of matter, is evidence, I think, that in nature there is something we may call—to name what never can be put into words—a Principle of Organization. Not only does it lift man ever higher but it provides three great essentials for his religion—it brings order out of randomness, spirit out of matter, and personality out of neutral and impersonal stuff.

These three contributions are of deep consequence to him. As to order, what oftenest persuades men that religion is untrue is a belief that the universe is purposeless, that all comes at last by chance. The hardest blow that Darwin struck at faith was not the proof that man had come from beasts but the assumption that the whole evolutionary process depends finally on variations that arise by chance. A living organism, however, is not a chance creation but a well-regulated system. It draws random matter in and endows it with order and directiveness. To see purpose in the lifeless universe may need the eye of faith, but *life,* at least, evidently moves toward goals. Here is assurance that in this part of nature purpose dwells; and if an organizing principle is manifest in life, may it not also exist in the wide harmonies beyond? As to spirit, we have explored with some success the possibility that this seemingly nebulous and unearthly thing is native to life itself, rooted in protoplasm, though ascending thence far up into the highest qualities that man can know. It is the supreme manifestation of the organizing power in nature. And as to personality, we know that in life this power makes individuals, persons, distinct and different. As life exists in individuals, so the spirit does in human personalities. The question of personality, in both man and God, is one of religion's ancient interrogations. If personality necessarily comes from the organizing power that is life, this is a fact of such immense significance that we should never lose sight of what it may imply.

This Principle of Organization, lifted far above its expression in matter and into the realm of spirit, may without irreverence, I believe, be thought of as an attribute of God. The very existence of spiritual qualities in man suggests that they are manifestations in him of something like them in the universe outside. They help to strengthen his belief in Universal Spirit. Whatever our idea of God may be, if He exists He surely must possess these spiritual attributes. Words are feeble things to express an idea so vast, but the conception of an organizing force, something that not only holds the universe together and builds within it orderly patterns of matter, from atoms and stars and galaxies to man, but con-

tinually lifts life upward from the simple processes of protoplasm to the highest levels of man's spiritual nature, seems
no unworthy expression of such an ineffable quality as God's
nature must possess.

To many this will seem a pallid substitute indeed for that
Almighty God whom they have worshiped; that Heavenly
Father who is their refuge, strength, and very present help
in trouble; that Lord of Hosts, eternal in the Heavens, before whose face the generations rise and pass away. On the
other side there will be those who find such a concept far too
mystical, too much like offering for worship the principle of
relativity or the self-regulating attributes of an electronic
calculator. If such a principle is that to which we must appeal to explain the development of animals and plants, and
if this same principle is to be magnified into a mysterious
Divinity, then we are back, they say, to where we must accept the ancient answer that what made living things was
God, an answer that at once removes the question from consideration by the intellect. We should remind all such ob-
jectors however that if God exists He must be manifest somehow in matter, and that His ways there are what science is
discovering. Out of lifeless matter came not only life but
those higher qualities in man which we have ventured to
call spiritual. Matter itself, by its very nature, may be such
stuff as leads inevitably to spirit. We must never underestimate its possibilities. Something in it, something that comes
out of it, may well be worthy of our reverence.

Whatever God may be, or whatever Godlike may exist in
nature, a vital question remains as to what contact we can
make with it. Man stands at the crossroads between matter
and spirit. From this strategic post he sees lifeless, unorgan-
ized matter being drawn into the bodies of plants and animals and there transformed into organized, goal-seeking,

living stuff. He sees a continuous and unbroken progression between this first step and the development of that most remarkable of all animals, man, with his far loftier goals and aspirations. The highest expression of man's life—the climax of the evolutionary process and still a biological fact —is his spirit, the inner, questing, desiring, aspiring part of him. To be sure, there is no proof that these things have relation to any higher form of spirit or that the human spirit can be divorced from its material bondage to the flesh. Nevertheless, the qualities that emerge in man which he regards as the highest that he knows, are the same *sort* of qualities he attributes to that greater Spirit in the universe. He is able to recognize and communicate with it only by means of his own spiritual sensitivities. Without the one he could not know the other. The human spirit, he believes, is a bridge to the Divine. Man's spirit, rooted in life, may actually be a part of the Universal Spirit, emerging from it and returning to it again.

For religion these concepts are of great significance. To think of God as a Principle of Organization may seem to make Him cold and remote; but we should remember that this expresses simply the minimum that biology requires to account for the phenomena of life. If the ideas presented here are sound, this organizing power that life displays is the basis not only of mind but of spirit. The Principle of Organization is far more than a scientific concept. It states a belief that there is operating in the universe something that leads to spirit, something that *is* spirit.

This is a tremendous idea, and its implications reach far out into the realms of belief and faith. It provides the basis for a conception of God that can fulfill the requirements of the rich and varied "overbeliefs" of men. If God is what everywhere brings form and order out of randomness and finally molds dead matter into something that gives birth to spirit, He can well be worshiped as Sovereign of the universe, of the lifeless as well as of the living. If man, however humble, shares this Universal Spirit, he should be able to make contact with it by that process of communion which through the ages has been known as prayer. If man's spirit is always expressed in human personalities, why may we not expect the greater Spirit, as well, to be manifest as a Person? If purpose is the essential quality of life, and thus of spirit, surely the Universal Spirit is not purposeless but moves toward some great end, some infinite goal. If this Spirit is limitless creative power, it can provide an inexhaustible reservoir of help and strength from which man can draw freely at his need. And if man's spirit is a part of that eternal Spirit in the universe, death may not exercise dominion over it. Just as it drew dead matter together to form the living body, so it may quit the body again and return to that unseen bourn from whence it came.

Such are some of the religious implications of this fundamental idea of an organizing, spiritual power in nature. Here we face problems so profound that final answers to them lie beyond the competence of science. It is not without significance, however, that the biological concept of an organized, goal-seeking, living system, whatever explanation we may find for it, can serve as the material anchorage for something that mounts far higher into the mysterious dominions of spirit.

All this, the theologian says, is simply to admit that man is a child of God, made spiritually in His image and with a divine spark in his heart. What we have called the human spirit, he continues, risen from simple biological purposiveness, is much more than meaningless emotion and may legitimately be regarded as an intermediary between the material and the Divine. Such a concept will startle the biologist, but it should reassure the man of faith by providing a reasonable means, through the aspiring, purposive nature of life itself, for a contact between man and God. Some would prefer to believe that the divine in man was planted in him directly by the Deity, and others that it developed during the upward course of evolution. The important point is that man's spirit, certainly an inhabitant of his living, material body, may without philosophical impropriety be regarded as similar in nature to a far greater Spirit, in which thus, literally, he may be said to live and move and have his being.

A Life Philosophy

The results of our excursion into these deep matters have been worth while, I think, in reaching an interpretation of life's unity that may help us understand more clearly what man's nature is. A further justification of such speculation, however, is that by its means one may be able to build a satisfying life philosophy. Try as he will, the man of science finds it hard to reconcile the orderly and impersonal determinism he sees in nature with the sense of freedom, personal significance, and spiritual values that is so deeply planted in his heart. In the inevitable choice that each of us must make between a philosophy founded on belief in spirit as the supreme reality and one that finds reality only in tangible and measurable things, decision comes more often from unreasoned preference and conviction than from rational argument. The crisis in many hearts today results from a clash between these two great monitors. Arguments drawn from science have often been opposed to traditional religious beliefs. The idea offered in these pages, however—that life itself is in its very nature purposeful and creative—provides a basis, I believe, on which one can formulate in scientific terms a conception of man's spirit that would otherwise seem to rest on faith or authority alone. There are hosts of men today who are convinced—though they cannot prove the truth of their conviction—that the universe makes sense only if it is interpreted in terms of freedom, personality, and spirit; in short, in terms of a philosophy that is essentially religious. As rational beings, however, they refuse to accept conclusions that are opposed to what their intelligence tells them is the truth. They seek earnestly to find a means by which reason and their inner convictions can be harmonized, to find in science a way to undergird rather than to destroy their faith. For such men the idea that high flowering of the spirit has its roots in the very quality of life itself may provide the foundation for a satisfying personal philosophy.

To many, of course, this seems a fantastic and mystical idea with nothing to support it in the conclusions of the sciences today. Certainly the orthodoxies of physics and chemistry reserve no place for spirit; but many biologists are coming to believe that the concept of *organism* is basic to the sciences of life and distinguishes them from the ones that deal with lifeless things. In this idea of organism, with the physical integration, the self-regulation, and the constant tendency to change that it involves, lies the essential germ of what has grown to conscious purpose and thus to what is called the mind; and of what in man, as we have seen, has led to the birth not only of his intelligence but of his spiritual sensitivities and aspirations. In life, and in life alone, there is evidence of something integrating, purposeful, and creative in the universe. As to what life is and whence its characteristic organizing power arises, we still are without an explanation. Here for the present we can only be agnostic and admit that the problem is not solved. It may be that with the advancement of biology and the broadening of its basis of ideas, an explanation in scientific terms will finally be made and the link between matter and spirit thus be forged. It may be that the origin of spirit lies in something deeper than the concepts of the sciences and goes back to an original creative spiritual factor in the universe which the intellect has no means of understanding. For the present, I think, we must accept the living organism as a *fact,* as something given in nature, as are the basic facts of the physical sciences, and around this we must build our conception of what life's meaning is.

Whatever the truth in these deep matters finally turns out to be, we may conclude, I think, that spirit is reality. The essential thesis of these pages is that the concept of the living organism makes it possible not only to bring body and mind into a unity but to recognize that man's *spirit* also has its source in the organizing, purposive, aspiring character of life itself. Life is the center where the material and the spiritual forces of the universe seem to meet and to be reconciled. Spirit is *born* in life. Here is a solid foundation for a philosophy that is truly religious. Man comes into a universe so vast, cold, and inscrutable that in it he feels utterly lost and insignificant—"a stranger and afraid, in a world he never made." The price he pays for reason is to be surrounded with problems that he cannot solve, with mysteries that seem unfathomable. In this cosmic darkness the little candle that is life is a comforting reminder that there is stirring here the germ of something like himself, something that can grow into a bright light on his course to show him the direction that he ought to take. Life is on the pathway toward the

spirit, and "reverence for life," in Albert Schweitzer's famous phrase, is the first step toward God.

In looking to life as the birthplace of man's spirit we must
remember that life is never static, but creative. In it new
goals continually arise. Nowhere has life's progress stopped,
and nowhere can we see a limit to what it may achieve. This
is the real significance of evolution—that life, and we as its
crowning product, may move ahead toward greater triumphs
of the intellect and higher spiritual insights. If we should
ever stop this progress and grow satisfied with what we have
and are, if we lose the adventurous spirit that still pushes out
across frontiers into territory as yet undiscovered, if we believe that we have apprehended final truth and close our
minds and hearts, then indeed is our race run and we are
doomed. Life's creativeness makes human progress possible,
but let us remember, too, that it never guarantees it.

This constant change in man's goals, this appearance of
new values that he seeks, is hard to explain by external factors, by conditioning and natural selection. His upward urgencies come chiefly from within, not from without, through
the emergence in him of new levels of aspiration. By looking
into man's personality we can learn much of what is significant and true. The human spirit is a glass through which we
can peer more deeply into reality than by purely rational
instruments alone. Man may not be the measure of all things,
but he certainly is the means by which we catch a glimpse of
what they are.

To all this, I think, religion should give heed. Life is the
visible expression of nature's organizing and creative power,
and can tell us much about what this power is and the ends
to which it moves. If life comes from God and leads toward
Him we can guide our course aright by seeking life's highest
goals. This is no easy thing, for lower ones are always clamor-

ing to be realized, and the aspiring spirit must often suffer frustration and disaster. Man cannot cope alone with all the problems that he has to face. Some therefore would persuade us, as a counsel of despair, that life inherently is sinful and that only by forsaking it and turning to God can we be saved. But if God is indeed life's highest expression, we shall find Him not by despising life but by magnifying it; not by abandoning it as evil, but by following where it leads, to that rich and abundant Source of it from which we can draw the strength and reassurance that we so desperately need. To do this is the continuing purpose of religion.

What is man's future? No one, indeed, can tell. "It doth not yet appear what we shall be." But that the future *may* be something finer than our dreams we cannot doubt—finer not in material and intellectual progress only but in spiritual understanding. The lesson to be learned from the biology of man's spirit is that what will decide his destiny are the goals of his desire. Hope for him depends on their being raised so high that he will lift himself upward in achieving them. He cannot be driven. He cannot be coerced. But he can be *led* by the drawing power of his desires. If what he wants is what the beasts want whence he came, he will go downward to their level. If higher goals can be implanted in his heart, he will climb upward to achieve them through tribulation and disaster. If he seeks to realize the loftiest ones of all, the aspirations of his spirit, though he cannot fully understand them now but only feels their urgency and power, his spirit will grow into completer harmony with the Universal Spirit and he may truly prove himself a child of God.

Such, then, is the conclusion of our adventurous attempt to bring together man's body, mind, and spirit as parts of a fundamental unity, three aspects of the same purposive, goal-seeking quality that is the distinctive feature of life at all its levels. The attempt is a courageous one, we may agree, but has anything come of it save an interesting speculation?

To many students of the processes of life the suggestions that have here been made will seem to introduce into the physical orderliness of the living system an element of mysticism that has no business there, and they may vigorously object to any idea of "spirit" in an organism. They may say that the concept of the body as a mechanism, operating by known laws of physics and chemistry, is the only one a biologist can profitably use. The "psychical" aspect of this mechanism is something that can be studied as process and behavior, but such inner feelings and experiences as it has, and especially its sense of purpose, are facts beyond the competence of science.

It should here be emphasized again that *whatever* the physical basis of organic self-regulation may turn out to be, it will still prove useful as a means of interpreting the phenomena of mind. An explanation of self-regulation at all levels may finally be made in purely physical terms. If so, the inner *awareness* of the process could still legitimately be regarded as the basis of purposiveness and all other psychical qualities. Perhaps we are, indeed, no more than goal-seeking automata, deluding ourselves with a sense of freedom and spiritual aspiration, but this sense is there and cannot be ignored. Perhaps the matter and energy of which we are composed may not bind us tightly but in their most complex expressions may actually emerge into something that, though still a mechanism, is a mechanism from which the life of the spirit is able to develop. Or perhaps, as is here suggested, there is some still undiscovered principle or process in nature that tends to pull matter together into living systems and is thus the basis of goal-seeking, both mental and spiritual. Some will be drawn to one of these alternatives and others to another, but we must all confess our present inability to solve the problem. Upon one basic fact, however, we may firmly stand—that living organisms move toward definite goals, both in their bodily development and in their behavior. It is this all-important fact—whether we account for it in terms of physics, chemistry, physiology, psychology, or theology—which, I believe, provides the intermediary between man's living, material body and those immaterial parts of him that are so closely interwoven with it.

This is no idle speculation but a most useful hypothesis on which to build a unified conception of man's nature and his relation to the universe. It interprets mind as an aspect of the same orderly directiveness that is evident in bodily development. It interprets spirit as the unreasoned urgencies and emotions that flow directly from this same source in protoplasm. It interprets motive as the tendency to move toward a goal, the sense of being drawn in our behavior, rather than driven. It interprets a goal as a norm set up in living stuff, to which its growth and activities conform; purpose as the intent to reach a goal; desire as the pull exerted, whether one purposes to reach the goal or not; and value as a recognition of the goal's desirability. It interprets beauty and goodness as values inherent in life itself, toward which life at its best continually tends. It interprets self, soul, and personality as the unique and individual knot of goals set up in an organism, which makes it different from all others and gives it a continuous history and significance. Finally, it interprets God as that Power which creates organized living systems and sets up in them the goals toward which they move and which culminate in the aspirations of the spirit.

Thus our hypothesis, based on a study of the development

of simple animals and plants, can help illuminate some of the deepest of man's problems by relating them to the goal-seeking quality that life invariably displays. They are all concerned with life and thus are finally problems of biology, but of biology in its widest and most inclusive sense, the biology of the spirit.

INDEX

Index